Regular Solutions

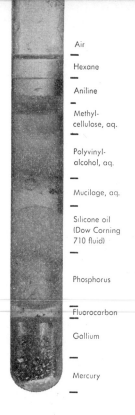

Air

Hexane

Aniline

Methyl-
cellulose, aq.

Polyvinyl-
alcohol, aq.

Mucilage, aq.

Silicone oil
(Dow Corning
710 fluid)

Phosphorus

Fluorocarbon

Gallium

Mercury

Ten stable liquid layers. An illustration of the problems chal-
lenging theories of solubility.

JOEL H. HILDEBRAND

Professor of Chemistry, Emeritus
University of California, Berkeley

ROBERT L. SCOTT

Professor of Chemistry
University of California, Los Angeles

PRENTICE-HALL, INC.

Contents

Regular Solutions

CHAPTER 1

The Regular Solution Concept

EVOLUTION OF THE CONCEPT

In a paper entitled "Solubility," published in 1916,[1] Hildebrand wrote:

> If we seek a clue of a kinetic nature to the deviations from Raoult's law, we find it in the limitation . . . that the molecules of the components must be sufficiently alike so that they are under the same forces in the mixture as in the pure liquids. It has seemed to the writer that the most satisfactory concept to serve as a basis for deciding whether the forces are alike or not would be found in internal pressure. . . . We shall endeavor to show, according to the evidence at hand, that approximate equality of internal pressures of normal liquids is an adequate criterion for . . . Raoult's law to hold.

A table of internal pressures was given and evidence was presented to show that, in the case of non-polar components, positive

---

[1] J. H. Hildebrand, *J. Am. Chem. Soc.*, **38**, 1452 (1916).

deviations from Raoult's law, with corresponding effects upon solubilities, increase with increasing differences in internal pressure.

In 1920, Hildebrand and Jenks[2] published the plot of the solubility of

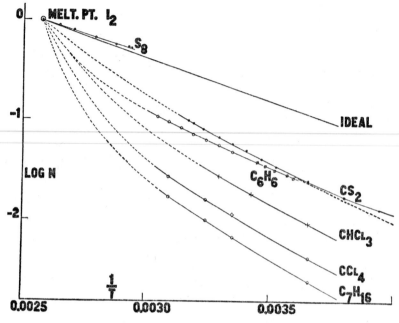

Figure 1.1 *Solubilities of iodine.*

iodine here reproduced as Fig. 1.1. (The symbol N was then used to designate the mole fraction of iodine.) They wrote:

It follows, therefore, that for solutions in which molecular changes do not play very important roles, the solubility data, when plotted in the above fashion, will give a family of curves converging to the melting point and approaching the ideal value calculated from the heat of fusion as Raoult's law is approached.

The line for the solution in benzene, obviously not part of the family, which is nearer to the line for carbon disulfide than to the one for chloroform, where it would be expected on the basis of internal pressures, was explained by solvation as follows:

If the solution . . . is cooled, the red color deepens, while if it is warmed, the color approaches the violet of iodine vapor, indicating that the solvation decreases with rising temperature, as would be expected.

This paper was followed the next year by one on the solubility relations

[2] J. H. Hildebrand and C. A. Jenks, *J. Am. Chem. Soc.*, **42**, 2180 (1920).

of rhombic sulfur,[3] for which at that time there were far more data than for iodine. Plotted in the same way, they exhibited a similar family of curves, in good accord with the relative internal pressures of the solvents.

In 1923, N. W. Taylor and Hildebrand[4] gave an extensive table of gas solubilities, in which these likewise followed the order of internal pressures. In 1927, M. E. Dorfman and Hildebrand[5] published a similar study of the solubility relations of stannic iodide.

During ensuing years, the solubility of iodine was determined in a great variety of solvents, as may be seen in Fig. 9.1. Iodine has been a superior solute for our purposes; first, because its concentration can be easily and accurately determined by titration, and second, because the simpler, "physical" solutions can be readily distinguished by their violet color from the solvated, "chemical" solutions. Evidence of regular, i.e., of nonspecific, interaction is now abundant.

The term **regular solutions** was first proposed[6] in 1929 in these words:

Evidently, the equations for the curves belonging to these families for systems which we will call *regular*, are to be sought before those of divergent and often highly individualistic curves of *irregular* systems. In the case of iodine, for example, the solvents which give a violet color, similar to that of iodine vapor, give regular solubility curves, while the solvents which give brown solutions give irregular curves . . . The writer believes it to be important . . . to distinguish the systems here designated as regular from those involving solvation or association, in order to gain a correct prediction of the temperature effect, and also that the change in volume on mixing should be taken into consideration.

If a solution is ideal, in the sense of obeying Raoult's law, the change in free energy corresponding to the transfer of a mole of component 2 from the pure liquid state to a large amount of solution, in which its mole fraction is x_2, (present notation) is

$$\bar{F}_2^i - F_2^o = RT \ln x_2$$

(see Appendix 1 for symbols.) The corresponding entropy change is

$$\bar{S}_2^i - S_2^o = \frac{-\partial(\bar{F}_2^i - F_2^o)}{\partial T} = -R \ln x_2$$

which thus depends upon composition only. From the standpoint of the interpretation of entropy in terms of probability, we can say that a mixture represents a more probable state for such a system than do the separate liquids. Now suppose that component 2 is transferred from an ideal solution to any regular solution in which it has the same mole fraction. From our picture of a regular solution as one in which orienting and chemical effects are absent, and in which the distributions

[3] J. H. Hildebrand and C. A. Jenks, *J. Am. Chem. Soc.*, **43**, 2172 (1921).

[4] N. W. Taylor and J. H. Hildebrand, *J. Am. Chem. Soc.*, **45**, 682 (1923).

[5] N. E. Dorfman and J. H. Hildebrand, *J. Am. Chem. Soc.*, **49**, 729 (1927).

[6] J. H. Hildebrand, *J. Am. Chem. Soc.*, **51**, 66 (1929).

and orientations are random, just as in the ideal solution, we may conclude that the probability of (component 2) is the same in the two solutions and, therefore, that the difference in entropy is zero. We cannot expect this conclusion to hold unless the random distribution of the molecules persists. We may expect, further, that a small correction should be applied to take care of the change in entropy accompanying changes in volume given by

$$\left(\frac{\partial S}{\partial V}\right)_T = \left(\frac{\partial P}{\partial T}\right)_V$$

or, we may state our principle in the following form: *A regular solution is one involving no entropy change when a small amount of one of its components is transferred to it from an ideal solution of the same composition, the total volume remaining unchanged.*

The final phrase has turned out to be far more significant than was realized at the time.

SEPARATE TREATMENT OF ENTROPY AND ENTHALPY OF SOLUTION

The great value of a generalization regarding the entropy of solution is that, if valid, it solves half of the problem of solubility. The Gibbs free energy of transfer from pure liquid component 1 to its mixture with a second component can be split into enthalpy and entropy of transfer:

$$\bar{F}_1 - F_1^o = \bar{H}_1 - H_1^o - T(\bar{s}_1 - s_1^o) \tag{1.1}$$

There is, of course, a conjugate equation with subscript 2's, throughout. Since

$$\bar{F}_1 - F_1^o = RT \ln\left(\frac{f_1}{f_1^o}\right) = RT \ln a_1$$

where f denotes **fugacity** (approximately, vapor pressure) and a denotes **activity,** then, if the solution is regular, and $\bar{s}_1 - s_1^o = -R \ln x_1$, and further, if there is no heat of mixing, $\bar{H}_1 - H_1^o = 0$, then

$$\frac{f_1}{f_1^o} = a_1 = x_1$$

which is **Raoult's law.** Deviations from Raoult's law can then be referred to the magnitude of the enthalpy of mixing. A general theory of regular solutions, then, depends upon discovering how to calculate enthalpy of mixing from characteristics of the pure components. Here, too, the concept of maximum randomness plays a primary role, permitting, as we shall see in Chapter 7, formulation of the distribution of contacts between like and unlike species of molecule.

QUESTIONS REGARDING ENTROPY OF SOLUTION

But let us consider first the validity of the concept that mixing can be virtually random and entropy ideal even in a non-ideal solution. The following questions must be faced:

1. *Do two molecular species with considerably different attractive fields tend to remain mixed in completely random fashion?* Or is there partial segregation on a molecular scale?

2. *What is the effect of marked difference in molecular size and shape?*

3. *What is the magnitude of the contribution of expansion?*

Evidence and arguments in answer to these questions are presented in Chapter 3.

Some writers have referred to regular solution theory as "solubility parameter theory." Although a valid theory of solutions must involve the heat as well as the entropy of solution, it is fitting to call attention to the facts: first, that the regular solution concept was based primarily upon the concept of maximum randomness and entropy; second, that this concept is simpler and is on a much firmer quantitative basis than the calculation of heat of mixing from solubility parameters. See especially Chapters 7 and 9.

THE TERM "STRICTLY REGULAR SOLUTION"

This designation has been used by several authors in senses which are more or less in conflict, not only with the concept stated above, but also with each other. Hildebrand commented upon these substitutions in 1951 as follows:[7]

The term "regular solution" has now come into general use, but not always in conformity with the above definition. For example, Guggenheim[8] uses it as follows: "We now turn to a class of mixtures called *regular mixtures* or *regular solutions* defined by the properties log $f_1 = wx^2/RT$—wherein w is not merely independent of the composition but independent of the temperature.—The name *regular solution* was first used by Hildebrand."

Rushbrooke[9] writes a certain partition function and says, "A solution for which the partition function is given by equation (8) is known as a *regular solution*." Longuet-Higgins[10] states:

[7] J. H. Hildebrand, *Nature*, **168**, 868 (1951). See also *Discussions, Faraday Soc.*, **15**, 9 (1953).

[8] E. A. Guggenheim, *Thermodynamics* (North-Holland Pub. Co., Amsterdam, 1949).

[9] G. S. Rushbrooke, *Introduction to Statistical Mechanics* (Clarendon Press, Oxford, 1949).

[10] H. C. Longuet-Higgins, *Proc. Roy. Soc.*, (London) **A, 205**, 247 (1951).

"This theory [of regular solutions] assumes that in a liquid mixture (a) the molecules are arranged in a regular lattice, (b) that the separate liquid components have ordered structures of the same type and (c) that the intermolecular potential energy is the sum of contributions from nearest neighbours in the lattice, the contribution of two neighbouring molecules depending only on their chemical nature."

I cite these differences not for the purpose of asserting my rights as the inventor of the term, but to urge that so useful a concept, to which a simple, definite meaning was originally attached, should not be robbed of its significance by different writers redefining it, each in his own way. I have no objection to a redefinition that may appear desirable in the light of present knowledge, but it should be made by general consent. To define the regular solution in terms of ideal entropy better fulfills the function of a useful reference state, well explained by Scatchard.[11] The student should be taught that

". . . thermodynamics deals with differences, that the number of differences to be considered can be reduced greatly by the use of reference states, that the magnitude of the differences can be reduced by the use of deviation functions, and that the choice of reference states and of deviation functions is entirely a matter of convenience, which should not be allowed to reduce the accuracy of any calculation. . . ."

In all of these models, the adjective "regular" is used in a sense that profoundly misrepresents the original concept.

Rowlinson,[12] in his valuable book, writes:

It seems, therefore, more useful to use the distinctive adjective *regular* for mixtures conforming to these equations.

His equations all assume symmetrical excess functions. Any such definition of regular solutions is so restrictive as to be of little use as a reference state. We shall see in the following pages abundant evidence that the heat of mixing is a function of volume fractions, not of mole fractions, and in but few cases are the molal volumes of the components so nearly equal as to lead to symmetrical excess functions. This is especially striking in the case of certain extremely unsymmetrical liquid-liquid systems, treated in Chapter 10, in which the molal volume of one component is as much as six times that of the other, but whose critical compositions can be accurately calculated by our formulation.

All of the substitutes for the original regular solution concept ignore the fact that virtually *all* systems are more or less unsymmetrical, and hence unamenable to the "strictly regular" equations.

[11] G. Scatchard, *J. Chem. Educ.*, **27**, 291 (1950).

[12] J. S. Rowlinson, *Liquids and Liquid Mixtures* (Academic Press, Inc., New York, 1959; Butterworth's Scientific Publications, London, 1959), p. 130.

Before proceeding with a consideration of evidence bearing upon the questions raised in this chapter, it is appropriate to present in the following chapter the thermodynamic symbols and relations which will be used in later chapters.

CHAPTER 2

Thermodynamic Relations

THERMODYNAMIC FUNCTIONS

It is assumed that the reader has at least an elementary acquaintance with thermodynamics, and that it is therefore necessary only to discuss the chief relations and symbols used in this book (see Appendix 1 for a summary of all symbols used in this book).

A Helmholtz free energy.
C Heat capacity.
E Energy.
F Gibbs free energy. The symbol G is widely used, but we are retaining the symbol used in the influential book by Lewis and Randall, recently re-edited and amplified by Pitzer and Brewer.[1]
H Enthalpy, heat content.
n Number of moles (Capital N is reserved for number of molecules).
P Pressure.

[1] G. N. Lewis and M. Randall, *Thermodynamics*, 2nd ed., rev. by K. S. Pitzer and L. Brewer (McGraw-Hill Book Company, New York, 1961).

R Gas constant, 8.315 joules/mole, 1.986 cal/deg mole, 0.08206 liter atm/deg mole.

S Entropy.

T Temperature, degrees Kelvin.

V Volume.

Extensive quantities per mole of substance are designated by small capitals; e.g., $\text{F} = F/n$, etc.

Partial molal quantities are designated by bars above the symbols for molal quantities, with the particular component designated by a subscript; e.g., $\bar{\text{F}}_1$, $\bar{\text{F}}_2$, $\bar{\text{S}}_1$, $\bar{\text{S}}_2$, etc. These partial molal quantities are defined as the rate of increase in the content of that particular (extensive) quantity *of the system* while that particular component is being added at constant temperature and pressure; for example,

$$\bar{\text{H}}_1 = \left(\frac{\partial H}{\partial n_1}\right)_{n_2, T, P}$$

The partial molal free energy of a component is often called its **chemical potential,** and it is designated by the symbol μ; e.g., $\bar{\text{F}}_1 = \mu_1$.

We use superscripts to distinguish states and kinds of processes, as follows:

^{g} gas	^{V} vaporization
^{l} liquid	^{F} fusion
^{s} solid	^{S} sublimation
^{o} standard state (in this book, always the pure liquid)	^{T} transition
	^{M} mixing
^{c} critical	^{E} excess (over ideal)
^{i} ideal	
^{r} regular (solution)	

Increments are denoted by Δ; e.g., ΔH, increase in heat content in a process; ΔH, increase in heat content per mole. Accordingly, for the heat of vaporization, we could write

$$\Delta\text{H}^V = \text{H}^g - \text{H}^l$$

The symbol p denotes vapor pressure, or partial pressure of a gas made explicit by superscripts and subscripts; e.g., p_1^o, p_1, p_2^s, etc.

The thermodynamic relationships we shall use most frequently are as follows:

$$F = H - TS \tag{2.1}$$

$$A = E - TS \tag{2.2}$$

$$A = F - PV \tag{2.3}$$

$$E = H - PV \tag{2.4}$$

(Note the alphabetical order and the negative sign.)

$$P + \left(\frac{\partial E}{\partial V}\right)_T = T\left(\frac{\partial P}{\partial T}\right)_V \tag{2.5}$$

$$\left(\frac{\partial P}{\partial T}\right)_V = \left(\frac{\partial S}{\partial V}\right)_T \tag{2.6}$$

$$\left(\frac{\partial F}{\partial P}\right)_T = V \tag{2.7}$$

$$\left(\frac{\partial F}{\partial T}\right)_P = -S \tag{2.8}$$

For the coefficient of thermal expansion we write

$$\alpha = \frac{1}{V}\left(\frac{\partial V}{\partial T}\right)_P = \left(\frac{\partial \ln V}{\partial T}\right)_P \tag{2.9}$$

The values of α found in tables are frequently $(1/V_0)(\partial V/\partial T)_P$, where V_0 is the volume at a reference temperature; for example, 25°C. The coefficient of isothermal compressibility is

$$\beta = -\left(\frac{\partial \ln V}{\partial P}\right)_T \tag{2.10}$$

The function $(\partial P/\partial T)_V$ we shall call the **isochore.** It is, of course, equal to α/β if α is defined by Eqn. 2.9.

We shall have occasion to use the term **fugacity,** designated f, introduced by G. N. Lewis as a measure of thermodynamic "escaping tendency." It is an effective gas pressure corrected for deviations from the perfect gas laws. The fugacity of a substance in two states is related to its molal free energy in the two states by the equation

$$F_B - F_A = RT \ln\left(\frac{f_B}{f_A}\right) \tag{2.11}$$

We shall make frequent use of the equation

$$F_1 - F_1^o = RT \ln\left(\frac{f_1}{f_1^o}\right) \tag{2.12}$$

for the free energy of transfer of a mole of, for example, component 1 from pure liquid to solution. Whenever gas pressure obeys the ideal gas law with what is considered desired accuracy, fugacity can be replaced by gas pressure. For methods of calculating fugacity, see Lewis and Randall.[2]

The composition of a solution can be expressed in a variety of ways; e.g., (1) concentration in grams or moles per unit volume; (2) the ratio of the number of moles of one component of a binary solution to the number of moles of a second component; e.g., n_1/n_2; (3) **mole fraction,**

[2] Reference 1, pp. 186–189.

$$x_1 = \frac{n_1}{n_1 + n_2 + \dots}$$

or (4) **volume fraction**; e.g.,

$$\phi_1 = \frac{V_1}{V_1 + V_2 + \dots} = \frac{n_1 v_1}{n_1 v_1 + n_2 v_2 + \dots}$$

It should be noted that the volume of a solution is not strictly equal to the sum of the volumes of its components, but is the fractional sum of its partial molal volumes; i.e., for a binary solution,

$$V = n_1 \bar{v}_1 + n_2 \bar{v}_2 \quad \text{and} \quad v = x_1 \bar{v}_1 + x_2 \bar{v}_2 \tag{2.13}$$

Volume fractions are extensively used in dealing with non-electrolyte solutions because they allow for the effect of size differences upon the energy of mixing in a more nearly adequate way than do mole fractions. The simple theories invariably disregard the small volume change on mixing, and it is doubtful if it will ever be worth the extra effort to use the "true" volume fraction based upon partial molar volumes.

For the purposes of this book we shall use only mole fractions and "volume fractions" defined in terms of the molal volumes of the pure liquid components:

$$\phi_1 = \frac{n_1 v_1^o}{n_1 v_1^o + n_2 v_2^o} \tag{2.14}$$

Since the two liquids may have different coefficients of thermal expansion, the volume fraction of a solution of fixed composition may vary slightly with temperature; this we shall neglect. Indeed, for convenience, all the molal volumes in Eqn. 2.14 might well be taken at a single reference temperature, such as 25°C.

The **activity,** a, of a component in a particular solution is the ratio of its fugacity to its fugacity in some arbitrarily chosen "standard state." In dealing with aqueous solutions of electrolytes, it is customary to select the infinitely dilute solution as the standard state. The fact that activity so defined is altered if the nature of the solvent is altered is often overlooked. In this book, the standard state is invariably the pure liquid, extrapolated below the melting point when dealing with the solubility of solids. This convention yields equations of the same form for all components, and avoids a distinction, often quite arbitrary, between "solvent" and "solute." *Where we wish to distinguish the "solute" in a binary solution we use subscript 2.*

THE GIBBS-DUHEM RELATION

It is possible to change the composition of a solution in two thermodynamically equivalent ways, and, therefore, to equate the free energy changes. One process is to add dn_1

moles of component 1 to a solution composed of $n_1 + n_2$ moles of the two components. The increase in the partial molal free energy $\bar{F}_1$, may be written as

$$dn_1 \left(\frac{\partial \bar{F}_1}{\partial n_1} \right)_{T,P}$$

The other process is to add an amount of the same solution containing dn_1 moles of component 1 and the proportionate amount $dn_2 = (n_2/n_1)\, dn_1$ moles of component 2 and to distill out the dn_2 moles of 2, thus obtaining the same final solution as in the first process. The addition of more solution of the same composition leaves $\bar{F}_1$ unchanged, while the change on distillation is

$$-dn_2 \left(\frac{\partial \bar{F}_1}{\partial n_2} \right)_{T,P}$$

But

$$\left(\frac{\partial \bar{F}_1}{\partial n_2} \right)_{T,P} = \left(\frac{\partial^2 F}{\partial n_1 \partial n_2} \right)_{T,P} = \left(\frac{\partial \bar{F}_2}{\partial n_1} \right)_{T,P} \tag{2.15}$$

Making the necessary substitutions and equating, we obtain

$$n_1 \left(\frac{\partial \bar{F}_1}{\partial n_1} \right)_{T,P} + n_2 \left(\frac{\partial \bar{F}_2}{\partial n_1} \right)_{T,P} = 0 \tag{2.16}$$

Had we considered the change in $\bar{F}_2$ in the same processes, we would have obtained

$$n_1 \left(\frac{\partial \bar{F}_1}{\partial n_2} \right)_{T,P} + n_2 \left(\frac{\partial \bar{F}_2}{\partial n_2} \right)_{T,P} = 0 \tag{2.17}$$

The independent variable may be left out, and the equations may be written as

$$n_1 d\bar{F}_1 + n_2 d\bar{F}_2 = 0 \tag{2.18}$$

This equation was first derived by Gibbs,[3] although it is usually attributed to Duhem[4] or to Margules.[5] In view of the number of "Gibbs equations," we designate this one and its equivalent forms as the "Gibbs-Duhem equation." It can be transformed into

$$x_1 d\bar{F}_1 + x_2 d\bar{F}_2 = 0 \tag{2.19}$$

Again, since $\bar{F}_1 - F_1^0 = RT \ln a_1 = RT \ln (f_1/f_1^0)$, we can write either

$$x_1 \, d \ln a_1 + x_2 \, d \ln a_2 = 0 \tag{2.20}$$

$$\text{or} \quad x_1 \, d \ln f_1 + x_2 \, d \ln f_2 = 0 \tag{2.21}$$

and since $dx_1 = -dx_2$,

[3] J. W. Gibbs, *Trans. Conn. Acad.*, **3**, 108 (1875), reprinted in *Collected Works* (Longmans, Green and Co., 1931), vol. 1, p. 88, Eqn. 97.

[4] F. Duhem, *Comptes Rendu*, **102**, 1449 (1886).

[5] M. Margules, *Sitzungsber. Akad. Wiss. Wien*, **2**, 104, 1243 (1895).

$$\frac{\partial \ln a_1}{\partial \ln x_1} = \frac{\partial \ln a_2}{\partial \ln x_2} \quad \text{and} \quad \frac{\partial \ln f_1}{\partial \ln x_1} = \frac{\partial \ln f_2}{\partial \ln x_2} \tag{2.22}$$

In all these equations, n and x are interchangeable, as are f and a and, to the extent that vapor imperfections can be neglected, f and p. If the solutions contain more than two components, corresponding terms are to be added; e.g.,

$$x_1 d\bar{F}_1 + x_2 d\bar{F}_2 + x_3 d\bar{F}_3 + \ldots = 0 \tag{2.23}$$

Equations analogous to Eqns. 2.16 and 2.23 can be derived for each of the other partial molal quantities; e.g., $\bar{s}_1$ and $\bar{s}_2$, $\bar{H}_1$ and $\bar{H}_2$, $\bar{V}_1$ and $\bar{V}_2$, etc., either by repetition of the same kind of argument or by differentiating Eqn. 2.16 or Eqn. 2.23 with respect to temperature, pressure, etc. at constant composition.

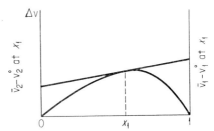

Figure 2.1   Graphic relation between partial and total thermodynamic quantities.

There is a simple, graphical method for determining partial molal quantities from a plot of the total quantity per mole of mixture. We illustrate it using partial molal volumes $\bar{V}_1$ and $\bar{V}_2$ in a mixture of two components with molal volumes v_1^o and v_2^o expanding when mixed by the amount Δv at constant temperature. The variation of Δv with composition of such a mixture is represented in Fig. 2.1. Since

$$\Delta v = x_1(\bar{V}_1 - v_1^o) + x_2(\bar{V}_2 - v_2^o)$$

the slope of the tangent to the curve at x_1 is

$$\frac{d\Delta v}{dx_1} = \bar{V}_1 - v_1^o - (\bar{V}_2 - v_2^o)$$

But $d(\Delta v)/dx_1$ is also $(\Delta v - I_1)/x_1$, where I_1 is the intercept of the tangent on the axis at $x_1 = 0$. Combining these three equations gives

$$I_1 = \bar{V}_2 - v_2^o \tag{2.24a}$$

Similar treatment gives for the intercept at $x_1 = 1$,

$$I_2 = \bar{V}_1 - v_2^o \tag{2.24b}$$

This result is a perfectly general one for any molal thermodynamic property of a binary mixture, or any of the "excess" functions defined later in this chapter.

PHYSICAL SIGNIFICANCE OF PARTIAL MOLAL QUANTITIES

In addition to being a very useful tool, this graphical relation illustrates the very important feature that a partial molal quantity is really a property of the solution as a whole, *not* a property of the component in question. One must not succumb to the temptation of attributing this physical property to the molecules of one species alone. For example, the partial molal volume of a solute must not be looked at as Avogadro's number N_0 times "the volume actually occupied by a solute molecule." The fact that the partial molal volume of I_2 at high dilution in perfluoroheptane is 100 cc, far greater than the 59 cc, which is the extrapolated value for pure liquid I_2, does not necessarily mean that the solute molecules occupy proportionately bigger holes. The partial molal volume is the total volume increase when solute molecules are added; a major part of this increase is surely due to a change in the packing of the adjacent solvent molecules.

THE IDEAL SOLUTION

The ideal solution offers advantages similar to those furnished by the concept of the ideal gas. Just as the law of the ideal gas suffices to describe the behavior of actual gases as a first approximation, so do the laws of the ideal solution suffice to describe actual solutions within certain limits. In both cases the idealized limiting behavior can be either (1) defined thermodynamically by means of empirical expressions or (2) derived from idealized models of molecular systems. Both approaches lead to the same equations. We defer a discussion of molecular behavior to a subsequent chapter and give here the thermodynamic definition of an ideal solution: one in which **the activity equals the mole fraction over the entire composition range and over a nonzero range of temperature and pressure.**

$$a_1^t = \frac{f_1^t}{f_1^o} = x_1 \qquad (0 \leqslant x_1 \leqslant 1) \tag{2.25}$$

Whenever gas law deviations are sufficiently small to permit substitution of vapor pressure for fugacity, we may write Eqn. 2.25 as

$$p_1^t/p_1^o = x_1 \tag{2.26}$$

which we recognize as **Raoult's law.**[6,7]

[6] F. M. Raoult, *Comptes Rendu*, **104**, 1430 (1887); *Z. physik. chem.*, **2**, 353 (1888).

[7] At vapor pressures below one atmosphere, the differences between Eqns. 2.25 and 2.26 are of interest only to those attempting to make very precise experimental measurements. For a good discussion of these details, see J. S. Rowlinson, *Liquids and Liquid Mixtures* (Academic Press, New York, 1959), Chapter IV.

Several corollaries follow immediately from this definition. First, from Eqn. 2.25 we conclude that

$$\frac{\partial \ln a_1}{\partial \ln x_1} = 1$$

so from the Gibbs-Duhem equation (Eqn. 2.22) we conclude that

$$\frac{\partial \ln a_2}{\partial \ln x_2} = 1$$

Upon integration, this equation yields

$$a_2 = Kx_2 \tag{2.27}$$

which in this form, or as $p_2 = Kx_2$, we recognize as **Henry's law.**[8] The conclusion that whenever one component of a binary solution (the "solvent") obeys Raoult's law, the other component (the "solute") must obey Henry's law is one which follows necessarily from the Gibbs-Duhem equation and is not restricted to ideal solutions. For the ideal solution, however, since Eqn. 2.25 is valid for all mole fractions, the constant K may be evaluated at $x_2 = 1$, where the activity of pure liquid 2 is unity; i.e., $K = 1$. Thus, Eqn. 2.27 is identical to Eqn. 2.25 except for the substitution of subscript 2's for 1's, and both components of an ideal solution obey Raoult's law.

Transforming to free energies, we may write for the ideal solution

$$\bar{F}_1^t - F_1^o = RT \ln x_1 \tag{2.28a}$$

$$\bar{F}_2^t - F_2^o = RT \ln x_2 \tag{2.28b}$$

$$\Delta F^M = n_1(\bar{F}_1^t - F_1^o) + n_2(\bar{F}_2^t - F_2^o) = RT(n_1 \ln x_1 + n_2 \ln x_2) \tag{2.29}$$

In addition, if Eqns. 2.22 through 2.26 hold over a range of temperature and pressure, we may differentiate at constant composition and obtain

$$\bar{S}_1^t - S_1^o = -\left[\frac{\partial(\bar{F}_1^t - F_1^o)}{\partial T}\right]_{P,x} = -R \ln x_1 \tag{2.30a}$$

$$\bar{S}_2^t - S_2^o = -\left[\frac{\partial(\bar{F}_2^t - F_2^o)}{\partial T}\right]_{P,x} = -R \ln x_2 \tag{2.30b}$$

$$\Delta S^M = -\left(\frac{\partial \Delta F^M}{\partial T}\right)_{P,x} = -R(n_1 \ln x_1 + n_2 \ln x_2) \tag{2.31}$$

From the equation $H = F + TS$ (Eqn. 2.1) we obtain

$$\bar{H}_1^t - H_1^o = \bar{H}_2^t - H_2^o = \Delta H^M = 0 \tag{2.32}$$

Similarly, for volume changes

[8] W. Henry, *Phil. Trans. Roy. Soc.*, (London), **29**, 274 (1803).

$$\overline{V}_1^i - v_1^o = \left[\frac{\partial(\overline{F}_1^i - F_1^o)}{\partial P}\right]_{T,x} = 0 \qquad (2.33a)$$

$$\overline{V}_2^i - v_2^o = \left[\frac{\partial(\overline{F}_2^i - F_2^o)}{\partial P}\right]_{T,x} = 0 \qquad (2.33b)$$

$$\Delta V^M = \left(\frac{\partial \Delta F^M}{\partial P}\right)_{T,x} = 0 \qquad (2.34)$$

Thus, when an ideal solution is formed from the pure liquid components at constant temperature and pressure, there is no volume change and no heat of mixing.

NON-IDEAL SOLUTIONS

Except for the special case of ideal solutions, the activity of a component is not equal to its mole fraction; it becomes convenient to define the activity coefficient γ of a component as

$$\gamma_1 = \frac{a_1}{x_1} \quad \text{and} \quad \gamma_2 = \frac{a_2}{x_2} \qquad (2.35)$$

The various molal free energies can then be written

$$\Delta \overline{F}_1 = \overline{F}_1 - F_1^o = RT \ln a_1 = RT \ln x_1 + RT \ln \gamma_1 \qquad (2.36a)$$

$$\Delta \overline{F}_2 = \overline{F}_2 - F_2 = RT \ln a_2 = RT \ln x_2 + RT \ln \gamma_2 \qquad (2.36b)$$

$$\Delta F^M = RT(x_1 \ln a_1 + x_2 \ln a_2)$$

$$= RT(x_1 \ln x_1 + x_2 \ln x_2) + RT(x_1 \ln \gamma_1 + x_2 \ln \gamma_2) \qquad (2.37)$$

The first terms on the right-hand side of Eqns. 2.36 and 2.37 are ideal free energies of mixing, so the second terms are the excesses due to the non-ideal behavior of the solution. We call these **"excess"** free energies, a term apparently first used by Scatchard, and write them as follows:

$$\overline{F}_1^E = RT \ln \gamma_1 \qquad \overline{F}_2^E = RT \ln \gamma_2 \qquad (2.38)$$

$$F^E = RT(x_1 \ln \gamma_1 + x_2 \ln \gamma_2) \qquad (2.39)$$

It should be noted that the excess functions can be regarded either as (1) the excess of the free energy of the non-ideal solution over that of the ideal solution, or as (2) the excess of the non-ideal free energy of mixing over the ideal free energy of mixing. One refers to the system and the other to the mixing process (and should then perhaps be written ΔF^E, as we have done in the past[9]); they are equivalent, and we have chosen the name "excess free energy" (without the "of mixing" and the symbol Δ) for brevity.

[9] J. H. Hildebrand and R. L. Scott, *Solubility of Nonelectrolytes*, 3rd ed. (Reinhold Publishing Corporation, 1950).

Positive values of the excess free energy ($\gamma > 1$) are referred to as **positive deviations** from Raoult's law of the ideal solution, and negative values ($\gamma < 1$) as **negative deviations**.

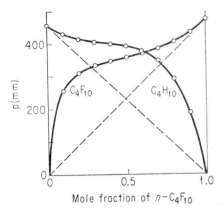

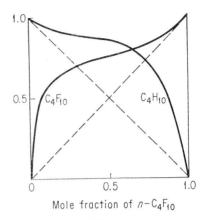

Figure 2.2 Partial vapor pressures of n-$C_4F_{10} + n\text{-}C_4H_{10}$ solutions at $T = 295.59°$K.

Figure 2.3 Activities in solutions of $n\text{-}C_4F_{10}$ with $n\text{-}C_4H_{10}$.

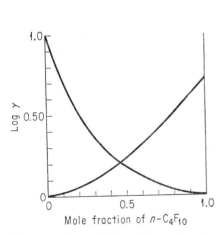

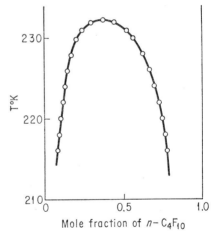

Figure 2.4 Log activity coefficients in solutions of $n\text{-}C_4F_{10}$ and $n\text{-}C_4H_{10}$.

Figure 2.5 Liquid-liquid solubility of $n\text{-}C_4F_{10}$ with $n\text{-}C_4H_{10}$.

Other excess functions: entropy, enthalpy, volume, etc., can be defined in a similar and consistent way. Since the ideal solution is formed with no heat absorption and no volume change, these excess functions are just the mixing functions themselves.

$$\bar{s}_1^E = \bar{s}_1 - \bar{s}_1^i = R \left(\frac{\partial \ln \gamma_1}{\partial \ln T} \right)_{P,x} = -\left(\frac{\partial \bar{F}_1^E}{\partial T} \right)_{P,x} \tag{2.40}$$

$$\bar{H}_1^E = \bar{H}_1 - \bar{H}_1^i = \Delta \bar{H}_1^M = RT^2 \left(\frac{\partial \ln \gamma_1}{\partial T} \right)_{P,x} = -\left[\frac{\partial(\bar{F}_1^E/T)}{\partial(1/T)} \right]_{P,x} \tag{2.41}$$

$$\bar{V}_1^E = \bar{V}_1 - \bar{V}_1^i = \Delta \bar{V}_1^M = RT \left(\frac{\partial \ln \gamma_1}{\partial P} \right)_{T,x} = \left(\frac{\partial \bar{F}_1^E}{\partial P} \right)_{T,x} \tag{2.42}$$

Examples of the variation of partial vapor pressures, activities, and logarithms of the activity coefficients with mole fraction are to be seen in Figs. 2.2 through 2.5 for mixtures of n-C_4F_{10} and n-C_4H_{10} at 295.59°K, from the careful measurements by Simons and Mausteller[10] at five temperatures. The deviations from Raoult's law are unsymmetrical and large. Below 232.2°K, the system breaks into two liquid phases at a critical mole fraction of n-C_4F_{10} = 0.39.

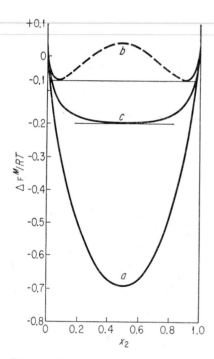

Figure 2.6 *Free energy of mixing: (a), one liquid phase; (b), two liquid phases; (c), at critical point.*

MISCIBILITY OF LIQUIDS

For ideal solutions and non-ideal solutions with small positive excess free energies, the curve of the free energy as a function of mole fraction is always concave upward (Fig. 2.6a). For large excess free energies there is a more complex curve with a region concave downwards (Fig. 2.6b); for such systems it is evident that one can decrease the free energy of the system by separation into two phases, and that the lowest free energy is represented by the points (representing a two-phase region) on a straight line simultaneously tangent to the curve at two points, which are, of course, the compositions of the two conjugate phases.

[10] J. H. Simons and J. W. Mausteller, *J. Chem. Phys.*, **20**, 1516 (1952).

Such a free energy curve has at least two points of inflection where

$$\left(\frac{\partial^2 \Delta F^M}{\partial x^2}\right)_{T,P} = 0$$

As the separation of the two conjugate phases becomes less, these inflection points approach each other and finally coalesce at the critical solution point (Fig. 2.6c). This critical point is thus defined by the conditions

$$\left(\frac{\partial^2 \Delta F^M}{\partial x^2}\right)_{T,P} = \left(\frac{\partial^3 \Delta F^M}{\partial x^3}\right)_{T,P} = 0 \qquad (2.43)$$

Substitution of Eqn. 2.37 for ΔF^M into Eqn. 2.43 and application of the Gibbs-Duhem Eqn. 2.17 yields another equivalent set of conditions for the critical point; see Fig. 2.7.

$$\left(\frac{\partial \ln a_1}{\partial x}\right)_{T,P} = \left(\frac{\partial^2 \ln a_1}{\partial x^2}\right)_{T,P} = 0 \qquad (2.44)$$

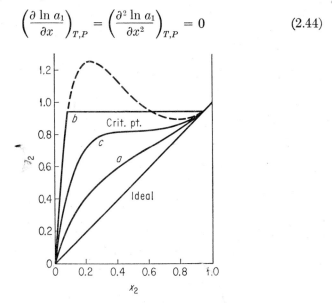

Figure 2.7 Activity of component 2 of a liquid mixture: ideal and a, single liquid phase; b, two liquid phases; c, at critical point.

ACTIVITY OF SOLIDS

If we use the pure liquid as the standard state, the activity of a solid substance is, accordingly,

$$a^s = \frac{f^s}{f^o} \qquad (2.45)$$

In dealing with the solubility of a solid, we shall have occasion to calculate its activity referred to the hypothetical liquid supercooled below the melting point. The equation

$$\left(\frac{\partial \ln a^s}{\partial T}\right)_P = \left\{\frac{\partial[(F^s - F^o)/RT]}{\partial T}\right\}_P = \frac{H^o - H^s}{RT^2} = \frac{\Delta H^F}{RT^2} \qquad (2.46)$$

can be integrated from the temperature T to the melting point T_m under the assumption that the heat of fusion is constant, $(\Delta c_p = 0)$ giving the familiar expression

$$\ln a^s = \frac{-\Delta H^F}{R} \frac{T_m - T}{TT_m} \qquad (\Delta c_p = 0) \qquad (2.47)$$

Where the difference between the molal heat capacities of liquid and solid are known,

$$c_p^l - c_p^s = \Delta c_p \quad \text{and} \quad \Delta H^F = \Delta H_m^F - \Delta c_p(T_m - T)$$

where ΔH_m^F is the heat of fusion at the melting point. Integration of Eqn. 2.47 then gives

$$\ln a^s = \frac{-\Delta H_m^F}{R}\left(\frac{T_m - T}{T_m T}\right) + \frac{\Delta c_p}{R}\left(\frac{T_m - T}{T}\right) - \frac{\Delta c_p}{R} \ln \frac{T_m}{T} \qquad (2.48)$$

Were Δc_p zero, one would draw the obvious conclusion that the most convenient way to show the temperature variation graphically would be to plot $\ln a^s$ (or $\log a^s$) vs. $1/T$, since the relation would then be a straight line. This, the conventional method, is analogous to the similar treatment of vapor pressures and chemical equilibrium constants.

However, Δc_p is not zero, and for our purposes there are some real advantages in plotting $\log a^s$ (and later $\log x_2$) vs. $\log T$. Let us examine the linearity of such a curve. We rewrite Eqn. 2.47 in the form

$$\left(\frac{\partial \ln a^s}{\partial \ln T}\right)_P = \frac{\Delta H^F}{RT} \qquad (2.49)$$

and take the second derivative

$$\left[\frac{\partial^2 \ln a^s}{(\partial \ln T)^2}\right]_P = T\left[\frac{\partial}{\partial T}\left(\frac{\Delta H^F}{RT}\right)\right]_P = \frac{\Delta c_p}{R} - \frac{\Delta H^F}{RT} \qquad (2.50)$$

At the melting point T_m, $\Delta H_m^F = T\Delta s_m^F$, so the second derivative would be zero (and the curve straight, at this point at least) if Δs_m^F were equal to Δc_p. Table 2.1 compares these two quantities for a representative group of solid solutes. The ratio of Δc_p to Δs_m^F ranges from 0.4 to 2.1, on the average certainly closer to one than to zero.

It is therefore apparent that it is at least as good an approximation as Eqn. 2.47 to assume that

$$\Delta H^F \approx T\Delta s_m^F \approx T\Delta c_p$$

or

$$\left(\frac{\partial \ln a^s}{\partial \ln T}\right) \approx \frac{\Delta H_m^F}{RT_m} = \frac{\Delta s_m^F}{R} \quad \text{and} \quad \ln a^s \approx \frac{\Delta s_m^F}{R} \ln \frac{T}{T_m} \qquad (2.51)$$

Consequently, for convenience we use log T instead of $1/T$ as the abscissa in our graphs, but we correct the a^s curves for Δc_p, if it is known. It should be noted, however, that Δc_p varies with temperature, and that far below the melting point a value for a_2^s is subject to some uncertainty. When plotting solubility for a non-ideal but regular solution, Δc_p involves the partial molal heat capacity in the solution, concerning which we know nothing. The fact is that a plot of log x_2 vs. log T gives absolutely straight lines in the region where $x_2 < 0.1$, as illustrated in Figs. 9.1, 9.6, 9.8, whereas log x_2 vs. $1/T$ gives curved lines throughout.

Table **2.1.** THERMODYNAMIC FUNCTIONS FOR FUSION

Substance	Δs_m^F (cal/deg)	Δc_p (cal/deg)	$\Delta c_p/\Delta s_m^F$
H_2	2.0	1.9	0.95
A	3.35	2.16	0.65
I_2	9.67	3.9	0.40
S_8	0.75	1.6	2.1
P_4	0.47	0.5	1.0
SnI_4	10.73	5.7	0.53
Si	9.46	5.6	0.59
CCl_4	2.4	1.1	0.5

SOLUBILITY OF SOLIDS

As defined here, the activity of the solid refers to the same standard state as is the activity of the solute in solution. Consequently, if the solute activity a_2 is known or can be calculated as a function of mole fraction x_2, the equilibrium condition $a_2 = a_2^s$ suffices to determine the solid solubility. If the solution is ideal ($a_2 = x_2$), the "ideal solubility" x_2^i equals a^s, and Eqns. 2.47 and 2.48 become equations for ln x_2^i. In subsequent figures the "ideal solubility" is shown by plotting log a_2^s on the mole fraction (log x_2) vs. log T.

A complication arises when the solid solute exists in two crystalline forms, with a transition point T_t below the melting point T_m. Above the transition temperature, the solute in solution is in equilibrium with the high temperature form (β); below T_t it is in equilibrium with the low temperature form (α). At the transition temperature, the slope of activity vs. temperature changes, at lower temperatures becoming a function of the heat of fusion of the α-crystal, which, if we neglect Δc_p, is just $\Delta H_\beta^F + \Delta H_{\alpha\beta}^T$. We may just as well, however, set $\Delta c_p = \Delta s^F$ and write

$$\left(\frac{\partial \ln a^\alpha}{\partial \ln T}\right)_P \approx \frac{\Delta s_\alpha^F}{R} \approx \frac{\Delta s_\beta^F + \Delta s_{\alpha\beta}^T}{R} \qquad (2.52\alpha)$$

$$\left(\frac{\partial \ln a^\beta}{\partial \ln T}\right)_P \approx \frac{\Delta s_\beta^F}{R} \qquad (2.52\beta)$$

As illustrated in Fig. 2.8 by the example of CBr$_4$, the α and β solubility curves cross at the transition temperature T_t; the α-curve extrapolates to the (hypothetical or metastable) melting point of the α-crystal, not to the normal melting point T_m, which is that of the β-crystal.

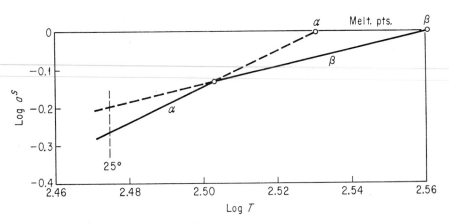

Figure 2.8 Activity of α and β forms of solid CBr$_4$.

The **entropy of solution** of a solid, $\bar{s}_2 - s_2^s$, may be related to the temperature coefficient of its solubility by means of the thermodynamic equation

$$\bar{s}_2 - s_2^s = -\left[\frac{\partial(\bar{F}_2 - F_2^s)}{\partial T}\right]_{P,x} = \left[\frac{\partial(\bar{F}_2 - F_2^s)}{\partial \ln x_2}\right]_{P,T}\left(\frac{\partial \ln x_2}{\partial T}\right)_{\bar{F}_2 - F_2^s, P} \qquad (2.53)$$

The second factor on the right is just the change of solubility with temperature at constant pressure if $\bar{F}_2 - F_2^s = 0$. In the first factor, $\bar{F}_2 - F_2^s = RT \ln f_2/f_2^s$, where f_2 is the fugacity of the solute in the solution and f_2^s is that of the solid solute. If the solid phase is pure solute (i.e., if there is no solid solution formation), f_2^s is not a function of x and we may write

$$\left[\frac{\partial(\bar{F}_2 - F_2^s)}{\partial \ln x_2}\right]_{P,T} = RT\left(\frac{\partial \ln f_2}{\partial \ln x_2}\right)_{P,T} = RT\left(\frac{\partial \ln a_2}{\partial \ln x_2}\right)_{P,T} \qquad (2.54)$$

Equation 2.53 thus becomes

$$\bar{s}_2 - s_2^s = R\left(\frac{\partial \ln x_2}{\partial \ln T}\right)_{\text{sat},P}\left(\frac{\partial \ln a_2}{\partial \ln x_2}\right)_{P,T} \qquad (2.55)$$

Since, at saturation solubility, $\bar{F}_2 = F_2^s$, we may write for the enthalpy of solution

$$\bar{H}_2 - H_2^s = T(\bar{S}_2 - S_2^s) = RT \left(\frac{\partial \ln x_2}{\partial \ln T}\right)_{P,\text{sat}} \left(\frac{\partial \ln a_2}{\partial \ln x_2}\right)_{P,T}$$

$$= -R \left[\frac{\partial \ln x_2}{\partial (1/T)}\right]_{P,\text{sat}} \left(\frac{\partial \ln a_2}{\partial \ln x_2}\right)_{P,T} \tag{2.56}$$

In the dilute region, where Henry's law holds (i.e., $a_2 = Kx_2$), or in the Raoult's law region ($a_2 = x_2$), $\partial \ln a_2/\partial \ln x_2 = 1$, and Eqns. 2.55 and 2.56 simplify to the forms

$$\bar{S}_2 - S_2^s = R \left(\frac{\partial \ln x_2}{\partial \ln T}\right)_{\text{sat},P} \tag{2.57}$$

$$\bar{H}_2 - H_2^s = -R \left[\frac{\partial \ln x_2}{\partial (1/T)}\right]_{\text{sat},P} \tag{2.58}$$

Equation 2.58, especially in the alternate form

$$\frac{\partial \ln x_2}{\partial T} = \frac{\bar{H}_2 - H_2^s}{RT^2}$$

is the "van't Hoff[11] equation" (one of several by that name) and is extensively used to obtain the heat of solution of a dilute solute.

SOLUBILITY OF GASES

The corresponding equations for solubility of a vapor above its normal boiling point are entirely analogous to those of the previous section for solids. The heat and entropy of solution follow the same van't Hoff type equation and the activity of a pure gaseous solute above the boiling point is given by Eqns. 2.49 through 2.52, except that the boiling point T_b replaces the melting point T_m and that the heat of condensation $(-\Delta H_b^v)$ at the boiling point replaces the heat of fusion. Because the heat of condensation is negative and the heat of fusion is positive, the temperature effects are normally opposite (approximately ideal solid solubility increases with temperature; approximately ideal gas solubility decreases with temperature).

Normally, the gaseous solute is so dilute that its molecules are nearly always surrounded only by solvent molecules. In this case Henry's law (Eqn. 2.27) applies, and it suffices to measure x_2 at a single pressure. We uniformly use the value at 1 atmosphere gas pressure; i.e., the inverse of the Henry's law constant expressed in atmospheres/mole fraction. Since

[11] J. H. van't Hoff, "L'équilibre chimique dans les systèmes gazeux ou dissous à l'état dilué," *Arch. Néerl.*, **20**, 239 (1883).

Henry's law is always obeyed, $\partial \ln \gamma_2 / \partial \ln x_2$ is always unity, and no corrections need to be made to the simple van't Hoff equations 2.57 and 2.58.

SOLUBILITY GRAPHS

It is evidently primarily a matter of convenience whether we plot the solubility of gases or solids as $\log x_2$ vs. $\log T$ or $1/T$, since the slope of the former curve yields $\Delta \bar{s}_2$, and the slope of the latter yields $\Delta \bar{h}_2$. Until recently reciprocal temperature was used almost universally as the abscissa, but with the resurgence of interest in entropy of solution Hildebrand[12] began in 1952 to plot $\log x_2$ vs. $\log T$, a practice we continue in this book. All the now extensive experimental data on solubilities of regular solutions, both of solids and of gases, when plotted in this way, give straight lines within experimental errors in the region where the mole fractions of solutes are less than ~ 0.1. This method has also the minor advantage that $\log T$ increases with T.

OSMOTIC PRESSURE

The osmotic pressure of a "solute" is the hydrostatic pressure that must be applied to a solution in order to increase the fugacity of the solvent to the value of its pure liquid at 1 atmosphere. This pressure is, by integrating Eqn. 2.7 under the assumption of constant v_1 (negligible compressibility) and combining with Eqn. 2.12,

$$P = \frac{RT}{v_1} \ln \frac{f_1}{f_1^o} = \frac{RT}{v_1} \ln a_1 \qquad (2.59)$$

The osmotic pressure is a convenient variable for experimental measurements, especially for high-polymer solutions and systems of biological interest. It also plays an important role in certain theoretical approaches[14] to the statistical thermodynamics of solutions. For our purposes, however, other experimental measures of activity are more useful, and we shall not use osmotic pressure in subsequent chapters.

[12] J. H. Hildebrand, *J. Chem. Phys.*, **20**, 190 (1952).

[13] The argument presented on a preceding page concerning the sign and magnitude of

$$\frac{\partial^2 \ln x_2}{(\partial \ln T)^2}$$

is invalid for gas solubilities, because Δc_p and Δs have opposite signs for the vaporization process. However, for gases far above the normal boiling point, the important quantities are the $\bar{s}_2 - s_2^g$ and $\bar{c}_{p2} - c_{p2}^g$, and there is virtually no information concerning the partial molal heat capacity of the dissolved solute.

[14] Cf. W. G. McMillan and J. E. Mayer, *J. Chem. Phys.* **13**, 276 (1945).

SOLUBILITY PARAMETERS AND "FORCE CONSTANTS"

We shall be dealing, for the most part, with liquids of widely varying intermolecular forces, cohesive energies, or internal pressures, which mix with considerable isothermal changes in heat content. In general, the attractions between molecules of different species are less than the arithmetic mean of the energies between the two like species, resulting, upon mixing, in expansion, heat absorption, and fugacities in excess of Raoult's law values. In Chapter 7, concerning heat of mixing, will be found a method for calculating these effects from properties of the pure component liquids. A useful parameter for this purpose, as we shall see, is the square root of the energy of vaporization per cubic centimeter. We designate it as a **solubility parameter,**

$$\delta = \left(\frac{\Delta \mathrm{E}^{\mathrm{v}}}{\mathrm{v}}\right)^{1/2} \tag{2.60}$$

A table of solubility parameters is given in Appendix 5.

In the case of gaseous components, we shall use the parameters of the intermolecular potential energy function determined from second virial coefficients, which Hirschfelder, Curtiss, and Bird[15] have called **force constants.** If the Lennard-Jones 6-12 potential energy for a pair of molecules (see Chapter 6) is written in reduced form,

$$u(r) = -\frac{\mathrm{k}}{r^6} + \frac{\mathrm{j}}{r^{12}} = 4\epsilon\left[\left(\frac{\sigma}{r}\right)^{12} - \left(\frac{\sigma}{r}\right)^{6}\right] \tag{2.61}$$

ϵ is the magnitude (depth) of the energy well at the distance of minimum energy, and σ is the (low temperature) collision diameter ($u = 0$ when $r = \sigma$). The energy "force constant" is usually expressed as ϵ/k in units of degrees Kelvin.

[15] J. O. Hirschfelder, C. F. Curtiss, and R. B. Bird, *Molecular Theory of Gases and Liquids* (John Wiley and Sons, New York, 1954). See especially Table I-A, pp. 1110–1112.

CHAPTER 3

Entropy of Mixing

RANDOM MIXING

Completely random mixing, and, therefore, regular entropy of mixing, are obviously not to be expected in mixtures in which the freedom of thermal motion is diminished by solvation, unequal association, or dipole interaction. But the question remains whether thermal agitation in mixtures of non-polar, reasonably symmetrical, molecules with considerably different attractive forces is sufficient to yield a virtually random mixture.

In the immediate neighborhood of the critical point, liquid-liquid systems, like liquid-gas systems, scatter light strongly. This scattering falls off rapidly, however, both with rising temperature and with changing composition. Zimm[1] obtained the figures in Table 3.1 for the system $CCl_4 + C_6F_{11}CF_3$.

Jura, Fraga, Maki, and Hildebrand[2] reported changes in vol-

---

[1] B. H. Zimm, *J. Phys. Coll. Chem.*, **54**, 1306 (1950).

[2] G. Jura, D. Fraga, Gilda Maki, and J. H. Hildebrand, *Prod. Nat. Acad. Sci.*, **39**, 19 (1953).

ume and heat capacity of the mixture of perfluoroheptane + 2,2,4-trimethyl pentane of the critical composition over a range of temperature spanning the critical point. The plot of heat capacity versus temperature

Table 3.1. RAPID DECREASE IN TURBIDITY ABOVE CRITICAL TEMPERATURE

t °C	Turbidity	t °C	Turbidity
28.31	>20	29.34	0.071
28.33	7	29.80	0.052
28.34	4.0	30.9	0.026
28.41	1.13	32.6	0.0144
28.50	0.56	34.7	0.0089
28.69	0.222	37.3	0.0061
28.90	0.150	47.2	0.0026
29.00	0.13		

showed a λ-type curve, and the curve for volume versus temperature was convex for a distance of a few degrees above the critical point. They wrote:

To avoid the complications caused by polar, and particularly by hydrogen-bonded molecules, we chose two non-polar components. In order to have limited miscibility, the intermolecular potentials within the two liquids must be very different. The potential between the unlike molecules in the solution is approximately the geometric mean of the like potentials, which is less than the arithmetic mean. Therefore, as mutual solubility increases with increasing thermal motion, 1-1 and 2-2 neighbors are replaced by 1-2 neighbors, with a decrease in the total intermolecular potential energy of each phase, causing expansion and absorption of heat. The connection between these two quantities is well recognized in the theory of regular solutions. Both increase more and more rapidly as the top of the liquid-liquid solubility curve is approached, but still continue, although at a greatly reduced rate, after the disappearance of the meniscus, because the mixing is still far from complete, as shown by the turbidity that persists in gradually decreasing degree as the temperature is further raised.

Conversely, on lowering the temperature of the critical mixture well above the critical region, there occur aggregations of like molecules of continually increasing size, as revealed by the beautiful work of Zimm. These remain suspended by Brownian movement until they become sufficiently large for the gravitational field to separate them into an upper and a lower phase. It seems obvious that the precise temperature at which this occurs is a function of the density difference and of the strength of the field, and might be measurably raised in a centrifugal field.

This last prediction was verified by Hildebrand, Alder, Beams and Dixon.[3] They found that at an acceleration of 10^8 cm/sec^2 the separation

[3] J. H. Hildebrand, B. J. Alder, J. W. Beams, and H. M. Dixon, *J. Phys. Chem.*, **58**, 577 (1954).

into two phases was raised by 10 deg. Most of this rise is the result of the hydrostatic pressure at the periphery, where the second phase appeared, of the liquid "above" the meniscus, since the separation is accompanied by a considerable decrease in volume. By varying the "depth" of the liquid in the cell in four stages from 13.5 mm to 6.5 mm and extrapolating to zero depth, the hydrostatic effect was determined and subtracted, leaving only 2 deg attributable to sedimentation, made possible by the large difference (1.017) in the density of the components. This 2-deg difference is small, in view of the large difference in density and the huge centrifugal field, 10^5 times the gravitational field.

Schmidt, Jura, and Hildebrand[4] carried out a very careful determination of the heat evolved in an ice calorimeter when a mixture of $CCl_4 + c\text{-}C_6F_{11}CF_3$ of the critical composition is cooled to 0 deg from a series of supra-critical temperatures. They thus obtained a curve from which the heat capacity at intermediate temperatures could be determined. A λ-type of curve was again obtained, whose supra-critical branch sank to horizontal within 6 deg. *Evidently the entropy, i.e., the disorder, had practically attained its maximum value within that interval.*

The rapid attainment of homogeneity with rising temperature is further attested by the sharpness of the maximum for sound attenuation over the consolute temperature measured by Chynoweth and Schneider,[5] here reproduced in Fig. 3.1.

Reed and Taylor[6] found that in mixtures of $i\text{-}C_8H_{18}$ with $n\text{-}C_7F_{16}$, the viscosity-volume fraction line shows a strong cusp at 23.7 deg, the critical solution temperature; the cusp is weak at 30 deg and non-existent at 35 deg.

The term, "clustering," may be misleading if it is interpreted as micro-drops of one pure component dispersed in the other. Hildebrand, Alder, Beams, and Dixon[3] wrote:

If these mixtures, in the region of light scattering, corresponded to ordinary emulsions, with globules of one density, the sedimentation could be analyzed after the manner used by Perrin. These mixtures differ from true emulsions, however, in that they have a cell-like structure, made up of micro-regions which contain the components in different proportions, separated by density gradients instead of abrupt boundaries. The components of a critical mixture are present in nearly equal volume, and the regions cannot properly be regarded as, respectively, outer and inner. As the temperature is lowered, the "cells" become larger and the composition gradients steeper, and eventually yield interfaces sharp enough to reflect

[4] H. Schmidt, G. Jura, and J. H. Hildebrand, *J. Phys. Chem.*, **63**, 297 (1959).
[5] A. G. Chynoweth and W. G. Schneider, *J. Chem. Phys.*, **19**, 1566 (1951).
[6] T. M. Reed and T. E. Taylor, *J. Phys. Chem.*, **63**, 58 (1959).

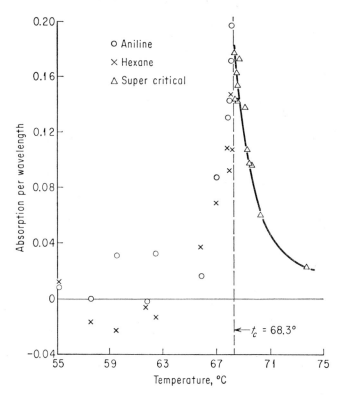

Figure 3.1 Behavior of the sound attenuation for the aniline-hexane system.

light. Separation into upper and lower phases is brought about by the action of gravity or of a centrifugal field upon the regions of different density.

All of the pertinent evidence supports the conclusion that, *except in the neighborhood of the critical point, clustering is negligible and thermal agitation causes practically random mixing.*

ENTROPY OF MIXING MOLECULES OF UNEQUAL SIZE

Before 1937, this question attracted little or no attention. Mixtures were known which, despite moderate differences in the molal volumes of the constituents, deviate less than 1 per cent from additivity in total vapor pressure. Examples are given in Table 3.2.

Table **3.2.** IDEAL SOLUTIONS FORMED BY COMPONENTS
OF UNEQUAL MOLAL VOLUMES

	$100(v_1 - v_2)/v_1$	$100\Delta p/p^i$
$C_6H_6 + 1,2\text{-}C_2H_4Cl_2$	12.7	0[a]
$C_6H_6 + CHCl_3$	10.1	0.6[b]
$CH_3I + CHCl_3$	28.6	0.5[c]
$n\text{-}C_7H_{16} + n\text{-}C_4H_{10}$	53.2	0[d]

[a] S. Young, *Fractional Distillation* (MacMillan Co., London, 1913), pp. 40–42.
[b] G. C. Schmidt, *Z. physik. Chem.,* **99,** 71 (1921).
[c] H. A. Beatty and G. Calingaert, *Ind. Eng. Chem.,* **26,** 504 (1934).
[d] G. Calingaert and L. B. Hitchcock, *J. Am. Chem. Soc.,* **49,** 750 (1927).

Stern,[7] in 1916, had shown that the number of arrangements of N_1 and N_2 molecules of two species in the lattice of a solid solution corresponds to an entropy of mixing of

$$\frac{\Delta S^M}{k} = N_1 \ln \frac{N_1 + N_2}{N_1} + N_2 \ln \frac{N_1 + N_2}{N_2}$$

This equation corresponds to

$$\frac{\Delta s^M}{R} = -(x_1 \ln x_1 + x_2 \ln x_2)$$

per mole of mixture, and to a partial molal entropy of transfer from pure component 1 to solution, in which its mole fraction is x_1, which is

$$\bar{s}_1 - s_1^o = -R \ln x_1$$

Hildebrand,[8] in 1937, showed that the same expression is obtained by considering the number of possible arrangements in line of two species of linear molecules, such as two normal paraffins. Two years later he and Sweny[9] reported measurements of the vapor pressure of hexane from its solution in hexadecane at 25°C, where, since the melting point of the latter is 16°C, a considerable degree of parallel array might be expected to persist. They obtained the following figures for p_1/p_1^o, the ratio of the partial pressure of hexane to its pressure over its pure liquid:

x_1	0.708	0.648	0.626
p_1/p_1^o	0.708	0.665	0.619

[7] O. Stern, *Ann. Physik,* [4] **49,** 823 (1916).
[8] J. H. Hildebrand, *J. Am. Chem. Soc.,* **59,** 794 (1937).
[9] J. H. Hildebrand and J. W. Sweny, *J. Phys. Chem.,* **43,** 297 (1939).

Raoult's law was thus found to be obeyed within the limits of error, despite a ratio of 2.25 in molal volumes. Recent measurements of Brønsted and Koefoed[10] show a small but unmistakable deviation from Raoult's law for mixtures of the normal paraffins: hexane + hexadecane, heptane + hexadecane, hexane + dodecane. Guggenheim,[11] as early as 1933, had called attention to the fact that a solution might be athermal but not ideal.

In 1937, Fowler and Rushbrooke[12] published a formulation of the statistics of a mixture in which one component occupies two sites in a fixed lattice, the other component one site. They found "that a mere change of size is sufficient to cause deviations from linearity; . . . though definite, the deviation is unexpectedly small for so large a change of size." A more general solution was given by Chang.[13]

The first attempts to calculate the entropy of mixing of long chain molecules with segments occupying sites of a lattice with small molecules occupying single sites were made simultaneously and independently by Flory[14] and by Huggins.[15] Modifications of this method have since been used by Miller,[16] by Guggenheim,[17] and by others.

This method of attack has served to account moderately well for the large deviations from Raoult's law of solutions of high polymers, which occur even in cases with virtually zero heat of mixing, where the entire deviation must be attributed to non-ideal entropy.

If molal volumes are used instead of chain-length of the polymer, these statistical, configurational analyses yield, as a simple first approximation for the entropy of mixing per mole of mixture,

$$\Delta s^M = -R(x_1 \ln \phi_1 + x_2 \ln \phi_2) \tag{3.1}$$

and, for the partial molal entropy of one component,

$$\bar{s}_2 - s_2^0 = -R\left[\ln \phi_2 + \phi_1\left(1 - \frac{v_2}{v_1}\right)\right] \tag{3.2}$$

where the ϕ's represent volume fractions. In the case of mixtures of common non-polar liquids, where the ratio of molal volumes is seldom in excess of 2, this formula yields figures not very different from $-R \ln x_2$.

[10] J. N. Brønsted and J. Koefoed, *Kgl. Dansk. Vid. Selsk.*, **22**, No. 17 (1946). See also A. Desmyter and J. H. van der Waals, *Rec. trav. chim. Pays-Bas*, **77**, 53 (1958).

[11] E. A. Guggenheim, *Modern Thermodynamics* (Methuen, 1933), p. 103. See also *Trans. Faraday Soc.*, **33**, 151 (1937).

[12] R. W. Fowler and G. S. Rushbrooke, *Trans. Faraday Soc.*, **33**, 1272 (1937).

[13] T. S. Chang, *Proc. Roy. Soc.*, (London), **A169**, 512 (1939).

[14] P. J. Flory, *J. Chem. Phys.*, **9**, 660 (1941); **10**, 51 (1942).

[15] M. L. Huggins, *J. Chem. Phys.*, **9**, 440 (1941); *Ann. N.Y. Acad. Sci.*, **43**, 1 (1942). (London),

[16] A. R. Miller, *Proc. Camb. Philos. Soc.*, **38**, 109 (1942); **39**, 154 (1943).

[17] E. A. Guggenheim, *Proc. Roy. Soc.*, (London), **A183**, 203 (1944).

A non-lattice derivation of Eqn. 3.1 has been given by Longuet-Higgins.[18]

Another basic question also presents itself: should Eqns. 3.1 and 3.2 apply only to a mixture of small molecules of one species with large, *linear* molecules of another, or also to a mixture of small molecules with large, *compact* molecules of another? In 1947 Hildebrand[19] proposed for the entropy of mixing $n_1 + n_2$ moles of two liquids the expression:

$$\frac{\Delta S^M}{R} = n_1 \ln \frac{V - n_1 b_1 - n_2 b_2}{n_1(v_1 - b_1)} + n_2 \ln \frac{V - n_1 b_1 - n_2 b_2}{n_2(v_2 - b_2)} \qquad (3.3)$$

where v_1 and v_2 are the respective molal volumes and b_1 and b_2 their intrinsic van der Waals volumes. This is an extension of the expression for the entropy of expansion of a one-component, van der Waals fluid,

$$nR \ln \frac{V' - nb}{V - nb}$$

It assumes, also, that the van der Waals "free volume" in the mixture is equally available to both components. It was stated that if the molal "free volume" of each component, $v - b$, is proportional to its molal volume, Eqn. 3.3 reduces to Eqn. 3.1.

It has not been possible until recently to make a very convincing test of the validity of Eqns. 3.1 and 3.2 for compact molecules, because of the scarcity of solutions whose components differ sufficiently in molal volume to prevent the effect upon entropy of mixing from being obscured by the ordinarily much larger effect of enthalpy. Recently, however, two solvents came to light whose molecules are at once non-linear and extraordinarily large. Octamethyltetrasiloxane, $(CH_3)_8Si_4O_4$, has a molal volume of 312 cc at 25°C; the tetraperfluoro-butyric ester of pentaerythritol, $(C_3F_7COOCH_2)_4C$, has a molal volume of 540 cc. We determined the entropies of solution of iodine in these solvents—both give violet, i.e., unsolvated, solutions—and we compared them with values in solvents having much smaller molal volumes. The molal volume of iodine is taken as 59 cc; therefore, the effect of the disparity in volumes, according to Eqn. 3.2, should be very large (2 cal/deg in the case of the ester).

In Eqn. 2.55 for the entropy of solution, the Henry's law correction $(\partial \ln a_2/\partial \ln x_2)_{P,T}$ is nearly unity for poor solvents, where $x_2 \ll x_1$, but is distinctly less in good solvents. In the case of iodine solutions in CCl_4 and CS_2, Walkley[20] obtained the Henry's law correction by measuring the partial pressure of iodine over the solutions; for other solvents it has been evaluated by the method described by Shinoda and Hildebrand.[21]

[18] H. C. Longuet-Higgins, *Discussions, Faraday Soc.*, **15**, 73 (1953).
[19] J. H. Hildebrand, *J. Chem. Phys.*, **15**, 225 (1947).
[20] J. Walkley and J. H. Hildebrand, *J. Phys. Chem.*, **63**, 1174 (1959).
[21] K. Shinoda and J. H. Hildebrand, *J. Phys. Chem.*, **61**, 789 (1957).

In Fig. 3.2 are plotted values of

$$R\left(\frac{\partial \ln x_2}{\partial \ln T}\right)_{\text{sat}} \quad \text{vs.} \quad -R \ln x_2$$

for a series of violet solutions of iodine in solvents of widely different molal volumes, as noted on the right of the plot. They are taken from papers by Shinoda and Hildebrand.[22] The points all lie upon the same line, evidence

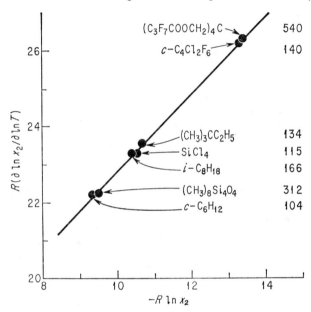

Figure 3.2 Entropy of solution of iodine not dependent upon molal volume of solvent.

that the wide range in molal volumes has no effect whatever. Specific interaction, however, as is exhibited by the non-violet solutions of iodine, very effectively diminishes entropy; the corresponding points for such solutions fall far below the line, as shown in Fig. 8.3.

Dyke, Rowlinson, and Thacker have made a comprehensive study of three systems, each composed of one fluorocarbon and one hydrocarbon, components with very different molal volumes, and report that "differences in the molar volumes of the pure components do not contribute appreciably to the large size of the excess functions of fluorocarbon and hydrocarbon systems." [23]

[22] (a) K. Shinoda and J. H. Hildebrand, *J. Phys. Chem.*, **61**, 789 (1957); (b) ibid., **62**, 292 (1958); (c) J. H. Hildebrand, *Zeit. physik. Chem. Neue Folge*, **16**, 245 (1958).
[23] D. E. L. Dyke, J. S. Rowlinson, and R. Thacker, *Trans. Faraday Soc.*, **55**, 903 (1959).

The principal error involved in transforming Eqn. 3.3 into Eqn. 3.1 is the assumption that in liquids the van der Waals free volumes, of the form $v - b$, are proportional to the molal volumes. Although this is true enough in gases, it is not so in liquids, as can be understood by aid of the purely thermodynamic equation:

$$\left(\frac{\partial S}{\partial V}\right)_T = \frac{1}{T}\left[\left(\frac{\partial E}{\partial V}\right)_T + P\right] = \left(\frac{\partial P}{\partial T}\right)_V \tag{3.4}$$

In gases, $P \gg (\partial E/\partial V)$, whereas in liquids the reverse is true. In liquids a change in entropy with expansion is primarily a matter of a balance between thermal energy and intermolecular potential, not one merely of the statistics of arrangements upon an imaginary lattice. The significant difference between linear and compact large molecules would seem to be that the segments of the former are partly free to interact individually with other segments and with solvent molecules.

THE CONTRIBUTION OF EXPANSION TO ENTROPY OF SOLUTION

In dealing with systems which deviate only moderately from Raoult's law, this question did not appear during the early years to be very important. The expansions that had been observed were usually less than 1 per cent.[24] That expansion is, nevertheless, significant was indicated as early as 1924 by the observation[25] that the relationship:

$$\log \gamma_1 = 0.105(\bar{v}_1 - v_1^o) \tag{3.5}$$

holds rather well for three mixtures:

$$C_2H_5I + CH_3COOC_2H_5; \quad CS_2 + CH_2(OCH_3)_2; \quad CH_3COOC_2H_5 + CCl_4$$

Scatchard,[26] in 1937, published the first quantitative analysis relating to the difference between excess entropy of mixing (over Raoult's law entropy) at constant pressure and at constant volume, and obtained the expression[27,28]

$$s_P^E - s_V^E = \frac{\alpha}{\beta}v_P^E - \frac{1}{2v\beta}\left(\frac{\partial \ln \beta}{\partial T} + \frac{\alpha}{\beta}\frac{\partial \ln \beta}{\partial P}\right)(v_P^E)^2 + \ldots \tag{3.6}$$

[24] Cf. J. H. Hildebrand and J. M. Carter, *J. Am. Chem. Soc.*, **54**, 3502 (1932).

[25] J. H. Hildebrand, *Solubility*, 1st ed. (Reinhold Publishing Corporation, 1924), p. 64; *J. Am. Chem. Soc.*, **51**, 66 (1929).

[26] G. Scatchard, *Trans. Faraday Soc.*, **33**, 160 (1937).

[27] Eqn. 3.6 differs from Scatchard's original paper by including the term $\partial \ln \beta/\partial P$, which he assumed to be zero.

[28] See also R. L. Scott, *J. Phys. Chem.*, **64**, 1241 (1960).

where v_P^E is the (excess) volume change at constant pressure. He then modified this thermodynamic relation with a derived relation between v_P^E and F_P^E, of less certain validity (see Chapter 8) and wrote, on the basis of the limited experimental data then available:

We may conclude that the volume change on mixing at constant pressure may be calculated approximately from the change in free energy or heat content, or may be calculated from the energies of evaporation of the components about as accurately as these two quantities. The effect of this volume change on the entropy of mixing is considerable, and it has a large effect on the calculation of the heat content change on mixing at constant pressure on the energy change at constant volume, but it has little effect on the calculation of the free energy change at constant pressure.

The final remark is important. The equation for correcting the Gibbs free energy of mixing at constant pressure to the Helmholtz free energy of mixing for the constant volume process, corresponding to Eqn. 3.6 for the entropy, is

$$\Delta F_P^M - \Delta A_V^M = F_P^E - A_V^E = \frac{1}{2v\beta} (v_P^E)^2 + \dots \tag{3.7}$$

Since the volume change is usually small and appears in Eqn. 3.7 as a square, the difference between the two free energies is normally trivial.

Most of the tests of the contribution of expansion to entropy of mixing have been made with systems which expand only a little upon mixing. For testing the role of any factor in a complex situation, it is important to select systems and conditions likely to make the role of that factor very large in comparison with other factors whose effects cannot be completely eliminated. This can be done for the relation between expansion and entropy of mixing by selecting components whose molecules have very different attractive fields. We have been obtaining the necessary data for applying rigorous tests to solutions of iodine, stannic iodide, and a number of gases, where expansion can be very large.

The correction to the partial molal entropy of solution of a dilute solute can be obtained from Eqn. 3.6 by differentiating with respect to n_2 or x_2, as follows [we neglect the term in $(v_P^E)^2$]:

$$
\begin{aligned}
(\bar{s}_2^E)_P - (\bar{s}_2^E)_V &= \left[\frac{\partial}{\partial n_2} \left(\frac{\alpha}{\beta} V_P^E \right) \right]_{n_1, P, T} \\
&= \frac{\alpha}{\beta} \left(\frac{\partial V_P^E}{\partial n_2} \right) + V_P^E \left[\frac{\partial \left(\frac{\alpha}{\beta} \right)}{\partial n_2} \right] \\
&= \frac{\alpha}{\beta} \bar{v}_2^E + (1 - x_2) \, v_P^E \left[\frac{\partial \left(\frac{\alpha}{\beta} \right)}{\partial x_2} \right]_{P, T}
\end{aligned}
$$

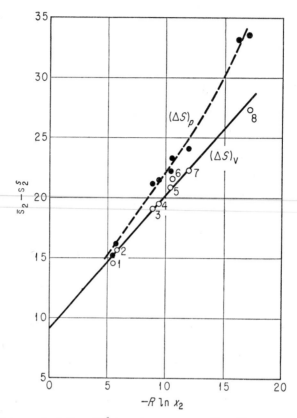

Figure 3.3   Entropy of solution of I_2 *at constant pressure,* $\Delta V = \bar{v}_2$, *and at constant volume,* $\Delta V = v_2^0$. *1,* CHBr$_3$; *2,* CS$_2$; *3,* CCl$_4$; *4,* c-C$_6$H$_{12}$; *5,* i-C$_8$H$_{18}$; *6,* SiCl$_4$; *7,* CCl$_2$FCClF$_2$; *8,* C$_7$F$_{16}$.

$(\partial V_P^E / \partial n_2)$ is, of course, the partial molal excess volume of the solute, $\bar{v}_2^E = \bar{v}_2 - v_2^0$. As one approaches the infinitely dilute solution ($x_2 \longrightarrow 0$), α/β for the mixture approaches the value for the pure solvent $\alpha_1/\beta_1 = (\partial S/\partial V)_{T,1} = (\partial P/\partial T)_{V,1}$, and the excess volume v_P^E for one mole of mixture approaches zero. Since $\partial(\alpha/\beta)/\partial x_2$ remains finite, it is clear that the second term vanishes as $x_2 \longrightarrow 0$, and we have for the very dilute solution[29]

$$(\Delta \bar{s}_2)_P - (\Delta \bar{s}_2)_V = (\bar{s}_2^E)_P - (\bar{s}_2^E)_V = \left(\frac{\alpha_1}{\beta_1}\right)\bar{v}_2^E = \left(\frac{\partial P}{\partial T}\right)_{V,1} \bar{v}_2^E \qquad (3.8)$$

[29] J. H. Hildebrand, *J. Phys. Chem.*, **64**, 370 (1960). The equation given in an earlier paper, J. H. Hildebrand and R. L. Scott, *J. Chem. Phys.*, **20**, 1520 (1952), is incorrect.

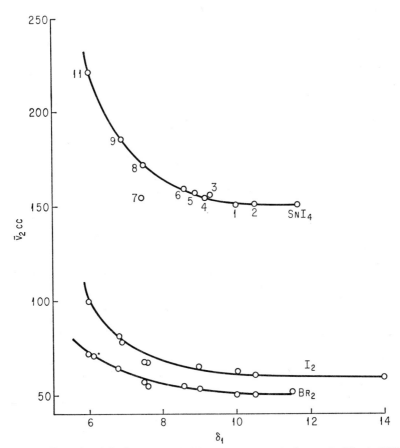

Figure 3.4 Partial molal volumes vs. solubility parameters of solvents. 1, CS$_2$; 2, CHBr$_3$; 3, CHCl$_3$; 4, C$_6$H$_6$; 5, C$_6$H$_5$CH$_3$; 6, CCl$_4$; 7, n-C$_7$H$_{16}$; 8, CCl$_2$FCClF$_2$; 9, c-C$_4$Cl$_2$F$_6$; 10, c-C$_6$F$_{11}$CF$_3$; 11, C$_7$F$_{16}$.

Values of $(\partial P/\partial T)_V$ for a number of solvents have been obtained by collaborators[30] of Hildebrand. Values for $\bar{v}_2$ for iodine have been measured by Glew[31] and by Shinoda.[32]

For representative iodine solutions relatively free from complicating factors such as polarity, marked geometrical asymmetry, and donor-acceptor action (slight with CHBr$_3$), Fig. 3.3 shows the ordinary entropy of solution, $\Delta \bar{s}_P$ (dotted line), and the calculated entropy of solution,

[30] (a) J. H. Hildebrand and J. M. Carter, *J. Am. Chem. Soc.*, **54**, 592 (1932); (b) B. Alder, E. A. Haycock, J. H. Hildebrand, and H. Watts, *J. Chem. Phys.*, **22**, 1060 (1954); (c) E. B. Smith and J. H. Hildebrand, *J. Chem. Phys.*, **31**, 145 (1959).

[31] D. N. Glew and J. H. Hildebrand, *J. Phys. Chem.*, **60**, 616 (1956).

[32] K. Shinoda, ibid., **62**, 295 (1958).

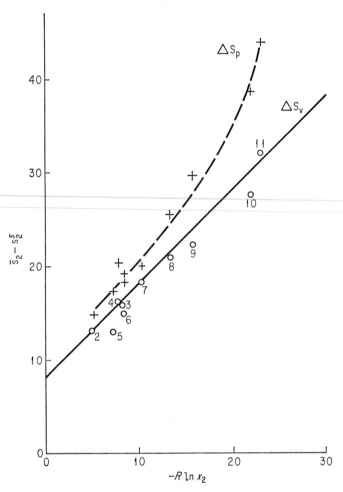

Figure 3.5 Entropy of solution of SnI_4 *at constant pressure,* $\Delta V = \bar{v}_2$*, and at constant volume,* $\Delta V = V_2^0$*. 1,* CS_2*; 2,* $CHBr_3$*; 3,* $CHCl_3$*; 4,* C_6H_6*; 5,* $C_6H_5CH_3$*; 6,* CCl_4*; 7,* $n\text{-}C_7H_{16}$*; 8,* CCl_2FCClF_2*; 9,* $c\text{-}C_4Cl_2F_6$*; 10,* $c\text{-}C_6H_{11}CF_3$*; 11,* C_7F_{16}*.*

$\Delta\bar{s}_V$ (the solid line), when sufficient pressure is applied to limit the added volume to v_2^0, the molal volume of liquid iodine, extrapolated. The slope of the line $\Delta\bar{s}_V$ vs. $-R \ln x_2$ is 1.10, close to unity, which it should be in order to conform to the original definition of a regular solution as one in which the entropy of mixing from the liquid state is $-R \ln x_2$.

    Smith and Walkley[33] have made the same calculations for solutions of

[33] E. B. Smith and J. Walkley, *Trans. Faraday Soc.*, **56**, 1276 (1960).

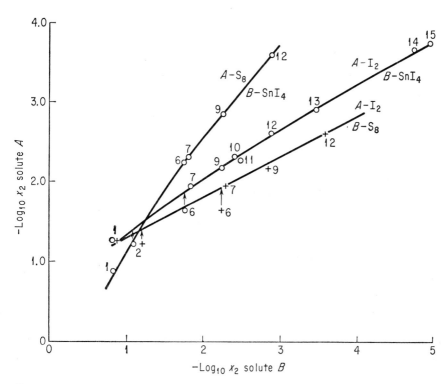

Figure 3.6 Regularity among solubilities of S_8, I_2, and SnI_4. 1, CS_2; 2, $CHBr_3$; 6, $CHCl_3$; 7, CCl_4; 9, n-C_7H_{16}; 10, $SiCl_4$; 11, i-C_8H_{18}; 12, CCl_2FCClF_2; 13, c-$C_4Cl_2F_6$; 14, c-$C_6F_{11}CF_3$; 15, C_7F_{16}.

SnI_4. Fig. 3.4 shows their values for its partial molal volume in very dilute solutions, together with the earlier ones for Br_2 and I_2 plotted against the solubility parameters of the solvent. This plot shows the effect of the enormous rise in $\bar{v}_2$ in proceeding from good to poor solvents.

Figure 3.5 is a plot for SnI_4 corresponding to Fig. 3.3 for I_2. The line has unit slope, and the intercept at $-R \ln x_2 = 0$ is very close to the entropy of fusion of SnI_4 extrapolated from its melting point by aid of the heat of fusion and the difference in heat capacity of solid and liquid. Further evidences of ideal entropy will be found in later chapters.

To summarize the foregoing presentation of the regular solution concept, let us recall that three more or less equivalent ideas have been used: (1) maximum randomness, (2) ideal entropy of mixing at constant volume, and (3) absence of selective, "chemical" molecular attractions. The third idea is illustrated by violet iodine solutions, and by simple correlations of solubilities with the solubility parameters of the solvents (see Chapters 4 and 9). A striking illustration of regularity in this sense is given in a paper by Smith and Walkley.[34] Figure 3.6, taken from their paper, shows correlations between the solubilities of three solid solutes in pairs, S_8, I_2, and SnI_4, in a variety of non-polar, non-complexing solvents.

It should be noted that this correlation is quite independent of the assignment of particular solubility parameters to either solute or solvent. In the case of solutions of I_2 in $CHCl_3$ and $CHBr_3$, there is a divergence, despite violet color. This may be the effect of the dipoles of the solvents.

An even more striking illustration of additive relations is to be seen in the case of gas solubilities, presented in the following chapter as a fitting introduction to further theory.

[34] E. B. Smith and J. Walkley, *Trans. Faraday Soc.*, **56,** 219 (1960).

CHAPTER 4

Regular Solutions of Gases in Liquids

ENTROPY OF SOLUTION

The entropy of solution of a gas can be calculated from the change of its solubility with temperature by means of Eqn. 2.55, with the entropy of the gas in its standard state, at 1 atmosphere, s_2^g substituted for s_2^s in that equation. We shall be dealing with sparingly soluble gases that obey Henry's law, hence we can write

$$\bar{s}_2 - s_2^g = R \left(\frac{\partial \ln x_2}{\partial \ln T} \right)_{\text{sat},P} \tag{4.1}$$

Until recent years, reasonably accurate measurements of gas solubility have been very scarce. Almost the only ones in non-polar solvents sufficiently accurate over a range of temperature to yield reliable figures for entropy of solution have been those of Horiuti,[1] for years almost unnoticed. Precise measurements for H_2 and D_2

---

[1] J. Horiuti, *Sci. Papers*, Inst. Phys. Chem. Research, Tokyo, **17**, No. 341, 125 (1931).

in a number of solvents were published in 1954 by Cook and Hanson,[2] and in 1957 by Cook, Hanson, and Alder.[3] Measurements of the necessary accuracy of the solubility of argon in five non-polar solvents were made by Reeves.[4] These last are plotted as $\log x_2$ vs. $\log T$ in Fig. 4.1. They

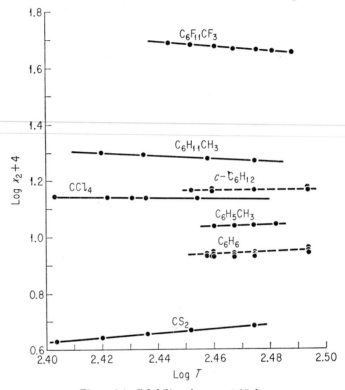

Figure 4.1 Solubility of argon at 25 deg.

reveal clearly the basis of the differentiation between positive and negative temperature coefficients of solubility. The mole fraction of argon in $c\text{-}C_6H_{11}CH_3$ is 18.55×10^{-4}; in CS_2 it is 4.87×10^{-4}. The corresponding entropies of solution are -0.9 and $+1.8$, respectively. If the solution in the former were diluted to the mole fraction of the CS_2 solution, it would add 2.64 entropy units to the -0.9 to give $+1.74$ entropy units, remarkably close, in view of the long extrapolation, to the value, 1.8, for the CS_2 solution, but not identical, because of the difference in heats of solution.

    [2] M. W. Cook and D. N. Hanson, University of California Radiation Laboratory UCRL 2459 (1954); *Rev. Sci. Inst.* **38**, 1957.
    [3] M. W. Cook, D. N. Hanson, and B. J. Alder, *J. Chem. Phys.*, **2**, 748 (1957).
    [4] L. W. Reeves and J. H. Hildebrand, *J. Am. Chem. Soc.*, **79**, 1313 (1957).

These observations by Reeves made it evident that the sign and magnitude of the change of solubility with temperature is determined in large part by the magnitude of solubility.

Further light was thrown upon the matter in a paper by Jolley and

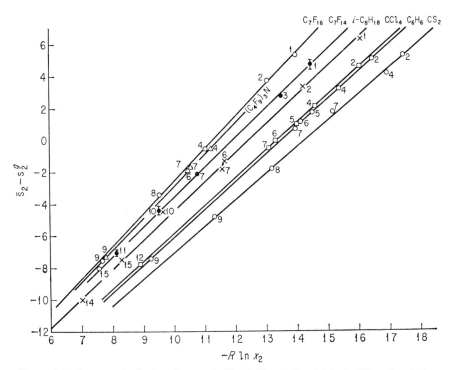

Figure 4.2 Entropy of solution of gases. 1, He; 2, H₂; 3, Ne; 4, N₂; 5, CO; 6, O₂; 7, Ar; 8, CH₄; 9, CO₂; 10, Kr; 11, Xe; 12, C₂H₂; 13, C₂H₄; 14, C₂H₆; 15, SF₆.

Hildebrand[5] in which the available data on gas solubilities were critically reviewed, and entropy of solution was calculated and plotted against solubility as $-R \ln x_2$. Subsequently, Kobatake and Hildebrand[6] added data on solubility and entropy for many more solutions (see Appendix 3), and gave the plot of entropy of solution vs. $-R \ln x_2$ shown in Fig. 4.2. The following features are to be noted:

1. *A regular system of relationships exists between entropy and solubility.*

2. The dividing line between positive and negative temperature coefficients of solubility is at $\bar{s}_2 - s_2^g = 0$, and there is a possibility of *predicting the temperature coefficient from a single value of solubility.*

[5] J. E. Jolley and J. H. Hildebrand, *J. Am. Chem. Soc.*, **80**, 1050 (1958).

[6] Y. Kobatake and J. H. Hildebrand, *J. Phys. Chem.*, **65**, 331 (1961).

3. *The entropy of solution becomes more negative in passing from the less soluble to the more soluble gases*, i.e., gases more like the solvent in intermolecular potential energy parameter. When $-R \ln x_2 = 0$, $\bar{s}_2 - s_2^\ell$ represents the entropy of a solution of a vapor at 1 atmosphere in a solvent in which it obeys Raoult's law; alternatively, it is the negative of the entropy of vaporization of the solvent itself to a hypothetical pressure of 1 atmosphere. Adding the entropy of expansion from 1 atmosphere to its vapor pressure gives a calculated value for the entropy of vaporization. The figures thus obtained are remarkably close, considering the long extrapolation, to directly measured entropies of vaporization. Three cases are given for illustration in Table 4.1.

Table 4.1. AGREEMENT OF ENTROPY OF CONDENSATION OF SOLVENT VAPOR FROM HYPOTHETICAL 1 atm WITH ENTROPY OF SOLUTION OF GASES EXTRAPOLATED TO $R \ln x_2 = 0$

	C_7F_{16}	$i\text{-}C_8H_{18}$	CCl_4
$-(\bar{s}_2 - s_2^\ell)$ at $-R \ln x_2 = 0$	22.9	22.8	23.3
$R \ln (760/P)$	4.5	5.0	3.8
Δs^V calculated	27.4	27.8	27.1
Δs^V measured	27.2	28.2	26.3

4. *The entropy of solution increases much more rapidly than* $-R \ln x_2$, indicating a contributing factor other than dilution in passing from the more soluble to the less soluble gases. This feature is clearly seen in Table 4.2, which is an extension of Table III in the paper of Jolley and Hilde-

Table 4.2. ENTROPY OF TRANSFERRING GAS AT 1 atm TO SOLUTION AT $x_2 = 10^{-4}$, AT 25 deg

		He	Ne	H_2	N_2	O_2	Ar	CH_4	CO_2	Cl_2
	ϵ/k	10	35	37	95	118	121	148	200	300
	δ_1									
C_7F_{16}	5.8	9.6	...	8.9	6.6	...	6.3	5.4	3.1	2.2
$C_6F_{11}CF_3$	6.0	8.7	7.5	...	...	...	5.5	...	...	...
$i\text{-}C_8H_{18}$	6.9	8.6	6.7	7.4	...	5.3	4.9	...	...	...
CCl_4	8.6	...	...	6.9	5.8	4.9	4.7	4.3	...	2.0
C_6H_6	9.2	8.5	...	7.0	6.3	5.4	4.9	4.8	1.7[a]	...
CS_2	10.0	...	...	6.2	5.6	...	5.0	3.4	2.1	...

[a] Solvated.

brand. This table gives the entropy of transferring gases at 1 atmosphere into solutions at the same mole fraction, 10^{-4}. Shown also are the solubility parameters of the solvents, δ_1, and the "force constants" of the gases, ϵ/k, from Hirschfelder, Curtiss, and Bird.[7] We see a moderate increase with decreasing δ_1-values and a large increase with decreasing force constants, corresponding to the fact that the range of the latter is much greater.

These data were interpreted by Jolley and Hildebrand as follows:

We interpret the differences in volume and entropy between different gases and solvents as follows. We reiterate, first, a point all too easily forgotten, namely, that what we commonly designate as a partial molal quantity of the *solute* is in reality what takes place in the *system* when a differential amount of solute is added. In the case of solutions so dilute as those here considered, these changes represent what happens in the immediate neighborhood of the solute gas molecules. These have low attractive fields and small volumes but possess the same kinetic energy as the molecules of solvent, hence the latter gain added volume and freedom of motion, the greater the smaller their force fields, such as they would gain at the surface of a bubble. Although $\bar{v}_2$ is a little larger for argon than for hydrogen in CCl_4, this must be attributed to its greater size (σ^3 is 40 $\mathring{A}^3$ for Ar, 25 $\mathring{A}^3$ for H_2) . . . The solvent around a molecule of hydrogen approaches more nearly to the state of a bubble than it does around a molecule of argon.

Walkley and Hildebrand found the remarkable differences shown in Table 4.3 between the partial molal volumes of H_2 and D_2.[8] These may be

Table 4.3. PARTIAL MOLAL VOLUMES OF H_2 AND D_2 cc AT 25 deg

Solvents		C_6H_6	$C_6H_5CH_3$	C_7F_{16}
H_2		35.3	35.7	54.4
D_2		32.7	32.4	52.9
	Difference	2.6	3.3	1.3

referred to the larger zero-point energy of H_2. Although the temperature is 25 deg, the gas molecules are confined in very small "boxes," tighter in the two aromatics than in perfluoroheptane.

Gas solubilities covering virtually the whole range of non-polar, non-reactive, gas solutions are plotted in Figs. 4.3 and 4.4, where log x_2 at

---

[7] J. O. Hirschfelder, C. F. Curtiss, and R. B. Bird, *Molecular Theory of Gases and Liquids* (John Wiley and Sons, Inc., New York, 1954).

[8] J. Walkley and J. H. Hildebrand, *J. Am. Chem. Soc.*, **81**, 4439 (1959).

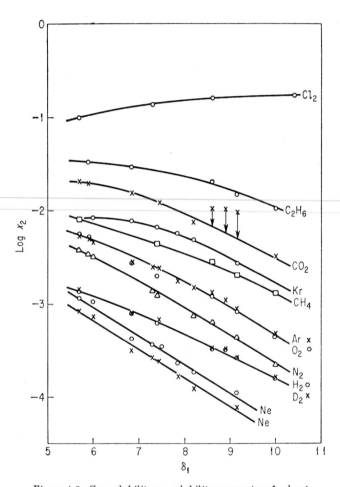

Figure 4.3   Gas solubility vs. solubility parameter of solvent.

25 deg and 1 atmosphere are plotted, in Fig. 4.3, against solubility parameters of solvents δ_1, and, in Fig. 4.4, against force constants of gases, ϵ/k.
The data used are tabulated in Appendix 3.

   The following features of these plots are to be noted:

   1. With certain exceptions, to be discussed, the experimental points
fall upon two regular grids. The spacing of the lines in the region of low
solubility is strictly in the order, in Fig. 4.4, of the force constants of the
gases, and in Fig. 4.3 in the order of the solubility parameters of the solvents. It is possible, accordingly, to predict with considerable confidence

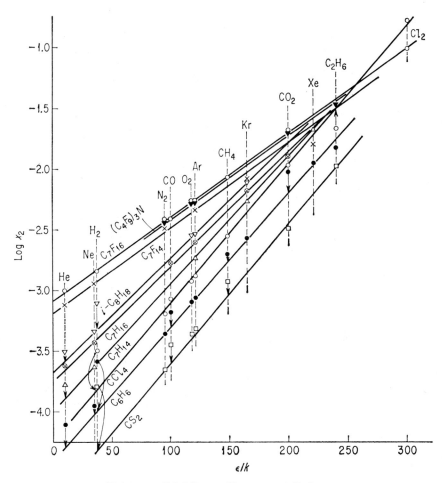

Figure 4.4 Solubility vs. "force constant" of gases.

log x_2 for missing cases, as well as to detect data of doubtful accuracy. A value of solubility having been predicted in this way, it is possible to predict its change with temperature with the aid of Fig. 4.1.

2. Cases of specific interaction are also indicated. For example, the point for CO_2 in C_6H_6 is above the line, as would be expected from the respective acid and base characters of these substances. The similar displacement for CO_2 in CCl_4 may arise from a similar solvation, as may be the case also with CO because of its reactivity.

3. The enhanced solubility of H_2 and, to a lesser degree, of He and Ne, may be referred in part to quantum effects, to be discussed later.

4. A gas whose force constant places it at the crossing of the lines for two solvents is midway between these solvents in its molecular forces. Also, Cl_2, in this respect, is closer to CCl_4 than to C_7F_{16}. A solution of Cl_2 in CCl_4 virtually obeys Raoult's Law.

The "grids" of relationships among solubilities, entropies, solubility parameters of solvents, and force constants of gases exhibit striking regularities in accord with the concepts of regular solutions. The entropy, except in the few cases of specificity, is clearly the sum of two factors: dilution and expansion. These factors are both determined by the interrelations of intermolecular forces as measured by solubility parameters and force constants.

Since, at equilibrium, the free energy of solution, $\bar{F}_2 - F_2^g = 0$, the many values we now possess for entropy of solution yield values for heat of solution, $\bar{H}_2 - H_2^g$. A valid theory of solubility must permit the calculation of these values from parameters of the components of the solution, such as δ and ϵ/k.

CHAPTER 5

The Liquid State

The preceding chapters have dealt mainly with the entropy of mixing. In regular solution theory, with its thermodynamic basis, this is one half of the problem; the other half is the enthalpy of mixing. The latter depends upon the potentials between like and unlike molecular species, their distribution in the mixture, and their relation to the thermodynamic properties of the pure components. To deal with these adequately is no simple task. The methods used by various investigators to relate these factors have been based upon differing concepts of the structure of liquids and the nature of the liquid state. Let us begin with liquid structure.

THE RADIAL DISTRIBUTION FUNCTION

A liquid composed of spherical, non-polar molecules has none of the long-range order characteristic of crystalline solids; the only ordering that exists is a short-range order resulting primarily from the fact that molecules cannot overlap. A convenient method of describing the structure

49

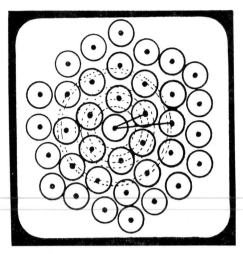

Figure 5.1   Model 2-dimensional random liquid structure, illustrating the meaning of the radial distribution function.

of liquids is provided by studies on x-ray scattering, such as those first carried out by Menke in Debye's laboratory. The probability that an element of volume dV in a liquid of volume V will contain the center of a particular specified molecule is, of course, dV/V. The probability that a given pair of molecules will occupy two such volume elements will be $(dV/V)^2$, provided that the distance r between them is sufficiently large that the intermolecular potential of such a pair is negligible, and that any order imposed by the packing of the molecules between is lost. When, however, the distance is small, approaching the order of magnitude of a molecular diameter, d_0, the volume of the molecules themselves and the forces between them help determine their positions. Then the probability that the given pair occupies the two specified volume elements is

$$g(r) \left(\frac{dV}{V}\right)^2$$

where $g(r)$, the "radial distribution function," is the correction factor applied to the random probability $(dV/V)^2$. Similarly, the probability of finding a particular molecule in a volume element dV at a distance r from the center of a fixed molecule is just $g(r)dV/V$. The number of molecules in a spherical shell of thickness dr (i.e., $dV = 4\pi r^2 dr$) is, therefore,

$$Ng(r)\frac{dV}{V} = \frac{N}{V}\,g(r)4\pi r^2 dr$$

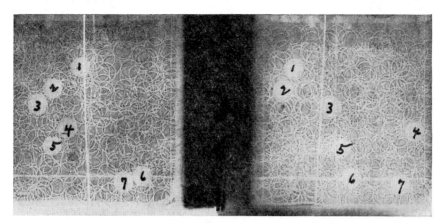

Figure 5.2 Determination of the distribution function of an artificial model liquid.

There are, of course, no neighbors within distances much less than one molecular diameter (g = 0). There is an enhanced probability (g > 1) for the first shell at $r = d_0$, a minimum probability (g < 1) between the first and second shells when $r \approx 1.5\ d_0$, and so on. This is depicted in two dimensions in Fig. 5.1. Debye and Menke[1] in 1930 determined from x-ray scattering the form of this function for mercury, here shown in Fig. 5.3a. This definition of a radial distribution function presupposed a spherically symmetric intermolecular potential energy function or, in the case of polyatomic molecules, that the general pair distribution function g_2 had been integrated over all orientations (angles).

Morrell and Hildebrand,[2] in 1934, obtained a function of the same form by use of a model. Gelatin balls of uniform size were made by letting drops of a hot gelatin solution fall into chilled oil. These were put into a portion of the same gelatin solution that had been boiled to prevent gelatinizing, contained in a cubical, plate-glass cell with coordinate axes marked on two faces. All the balls, except a few that had been blackened by adding a little lampblack to the solution, became virtually transparent because of identity of refractive index of uncolored balls and surrounding solution.

The vessel and contents were mechanically shaken, in order to secure random distribution of the balls; the shaking was stopped, and a photograph taken immediately by spark illumination of the two coordinate faces of the cell by the aid of a mirror. A typical photograph is reproduced

---

[1] P. Debye and H. Menke, *Physik. Z.*, **31**, 797 (1930).

[2] W. E. Morrell and J. H. Hildebrand, *Science*, **80**, 125 (1934); *J. Chem. Phys.*, **4**, 3 (1936).

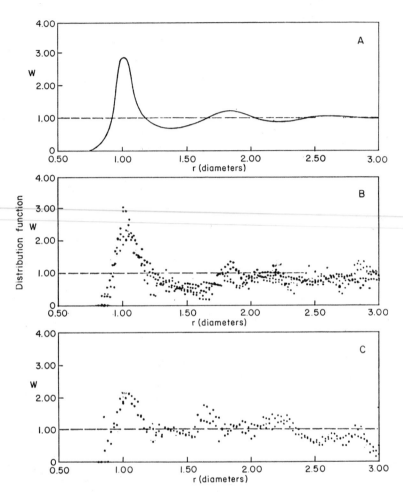

*Figure 5.3 Comparison of the distribution function of mercury, as deter-
mined by Debye and Menke from x-ray scattering, with that of the model.
The lowest pattern was obtained at a higher simulated temperature.*

in Fig. 5.2. The *xyz* coordinates of the marked balls were read from the
films and their radial distances computed. The distances found are plotted
vs. *r*/d in Fig. 5.3b. The distribution function obtained from this model
closely simulated that for mercury.

Higher temperatures and resultant expansions were simulated by sus-
pending fewer gelatin balls in the same volume. The peak becomes lower
and broader with rising temperature, as would be expected. See Fig. 5.3c.

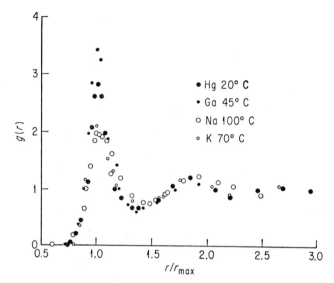

Figure 5.4 Comparison of the distribution functions of four metals.

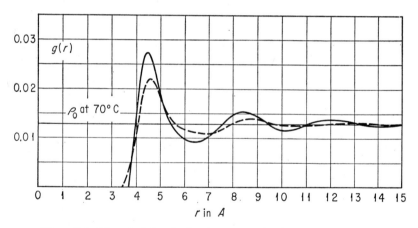

Figure 5.5 The actual density in atoms per unit volume as a function of distance from any one atom in liquid potassium at 70°C. The dotted curve (with slightly shifted ordinate) shows that for liquid potassium at 395°C.

In 1939, Hildebrand[3] superimposed the distribution functions of mercury, gallium, sodium, and potassium, as shown in Fig. 5.4, against r/r_{max}. The sharpest peak, as would be expected, is the one for gallium, the liquid

[3] J. H. Hildebrand, *Science*, **90**, 1 (1939).

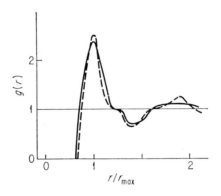

Figure 5.6 Distribution functions of argon and xenon at same reduced volume.

farthest below its boiling point. In 1939, Boyd and Wakeham[4] determined the distribution function of mercury at temperatures ranging from -36 deg to 250 deg, and found that the peaks become lower and broader with rising temperature, as expected. In 1938, Thomas and Gingrich[5] showed a similar change for potassium compared at 70 deg and 395 deg, as seen in Fig. 5.5.

In 1943, Campbell and Hildebrand[6] reported the same trend for mercury and for xenon, also that the function for xenon is virtually identical at 163°K and 1 atmosphere and at 183°K and 130 atmospheres, where the density is the same. They showed, further, that the normalized functions for argon and xenon at corresponding states agree very closely, as shown in Fig. 5.6.

THE NUMBER OF NEAREST NEIGHBORS

It has been not uncommon for investigators to assume that the number of nearest neighbors around a central molecule corresponds to some definite crystal structure, even as high as the close-packed number, twelve. Such assumptions can be checked by the aid of experimentally determined distribution functions. The number of molecules, N_r within the variable distance r is

$$N_r = \frac{4\pi N_0}{v} \int_0^r r^2 g(r) dr \tag{5.1}$$

[4] R. W. Boyd and H. R. R. Wakeham, *J. Chem. Phys.*, **7**, 958 (1939).

[5] C. D. Thomas and N. S. Gingrich, *J. Chem. Phys.*, **6**, 411 (1938). See also N. S. Gingrich, *Rev. Mod. Phys.*, **15**, 90 (1943); R. C. Ling, *J. Chem. Phys.*, **25**, 609 (1956).

[6] J. A. Campbell and J. H. Hildebrand, *J. Chem. Phys.*, **11**, 330, 334 (1943).

where N_0 is the Avogadro number. Upon plotting $4\pi r^2 g(r)$ vs. r for xenon under the three conditions stated above, the areas under the first peak as far as the first minimum gave the numbers of near neighbors within this distance, as shown in Table 5.1.

Table **5.1.** NUMBER OF NEAR NEIGHBORS IN LIQUID Xe

°K	P, atm	N
163	1	8.5
183	130	9.0
183	2.5	8.3

Similar results are obtained with other liquids. The number of nearest neighbors is far short of twelve.

Prokhorenko and Fisher[7] have given a detailed theory for fluctuation of the coordination numbers in simple liquids. They calculated the average fluctuation in the coordination numbers of Ar, Xe, Hg and several other metals to be greater than 20 per cent for the first coordination shell and ~50 per cent for the second. They conclude that these results contradict the concept of a quasi-crystalline structure for liquids.

LATTICE THEORIES OF LIQUID STRUCTURE

Many investigators have ascribed to liquids a certain degree of order not revealed by x-ray scattering. Stewart and Marron,[8] in 1927, proposed the term "cybotactic state," interpreted as a "space array not as caused by fragmentary crystals, but by a type of molecular arrangement wherein there is combined mobility of the component molecules and yet a recognizable space array." They admitted, however, that "A general conclusion of the universality of cybotaxis in liquids is not justified," adding that "Our present x-ray method does not show the cybotactic state clearly unless it becomes strongly marked by the use of long chain molecules."

In 1953, Hildebrand[9] published side by side negatives of x-ray scattering of gallium, made at his suggestion by D. W. Fraga, taken with the same sample and apparatus, one of the solid powder at 22 deg, the other of the liquid at 30.5 deg. The latter contains no trace of the well-marked lines in the former.

[7] V. K. Prokhorenko and I. Z. Fisher, *Zhur. Fiz. Khim.*, **33**, 1852 (1959).

[8] G. W. Stewart and R. M. Marron, *Phys. Rev.*, **30**, 232 (1927).

[9] J. H. Hildebrand, *Discussions, Faraday Soc.*, No. 15, 9 (1953).

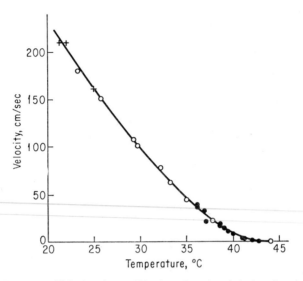

Figure 5.7   Velocity of crystallization of supercooled phosphorus.

The x-ray evidence has not, however, deterred a number of investigators from assuming some sort of quasi-lattice order, implicit in such terms as "lattice sites," "cell theory," "hole theory," the existence side by side of "gas-like" and "solid-like molecules."

These concepts of liquid structure can hardly be reconciled with the following experimental facts:

EVIDENCE FOR MAXIMUM RANDOMNESS

1. *The existence of super-cooled liquid* P_4 *from the melting point,* 44.1 deg, *as far as* −71 deg was found by Hildebrand and Rotariu,[10] who also kept the substance in liquid form at room temperatures "for months at a time." They wrote:

The ability of the liquid to survive such low temperatures may be explained in part by the comparatively small free energy of the process in the light of the small heat of fusion. But the fact that the pure liquid persists indefinitely at room temperatures shows that the barrier against crystallization is a very real and effective one, and seems to show the inadequacy of the assumption so often made in dealing with the liquid state that the structure is quasi-crystalline, being either that of a slightly mussed up, close-packed solid, or a regular lattice, with holes here and there. One would think that phosphorus would not remain liquid so long if crystallization could be started simply by a few molecules moving into adjacent holes.

[10] J. H. Hildebrand and G. J. Rotariu, *J. Am. Chem. Soc.,* **73,** 2524 (1951).

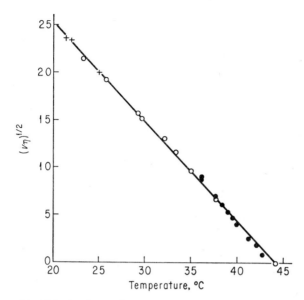

Figure 5.8 Velocity of crystallization, V, of supercooled phosphorus. Test of relation $(V\eta)^{1/2} = K(44.1 - t)$.

Solid P_4 behaves like a solid with rotating molecules; there is a transition[11] at -76.9 deg from cubic to hexagonal structure and the entropy of fusion[12] is 1.984 cal/deg. The large supercooling is not the result of low velocity of crystallization; Powell, Gilman, and Hildebrand[13] measured a reproducible, linear velocity at 22 deg of 210 cm per second. See Figs. 5.7 and 5.8.

2. *The temperature coefficient of diffusion at constant volume* for I_2 in CCl_4 was determined by Haycock, Alder and Hildebrand.[14] In discussing their results, they wrote:

This investigation was undertaken in the hope of testing the relative applicability of two models of diffusion; the one, in which a molecule moves into an adjacent hole, the other in which two molecules have sufficient kinetic energy in opposite directions to exchange places, overcoming repulsive forces and pushing neighboring molecules aside. In the first model it is frequently assumed that the rate-determining step of diffusion is the formation of the hole, and hence the activation energy for

[11] D. M. Yost and H. Russell, *Systematic Inorganic Chemistry* (Prentice-Hall, Inc., New York, 1944).

[12] C. C. Stephenson, private communication.

[13] R. E. Powell, T. S. Gilman, and J. H. Hildebrand, *J. Am. Chem. Soc.*, **73**, 2525 (1951).

[14] E. W. Haycock, B. J. Alder, and J. H. Hildebrand, *J. Chem. Phys.*, **21**, 1601 (1953).

diffusion is determined by the energy necessary for this process. Furthermore, with this model, the diffusion depends predominantly upon the number of holes and hence, at constant volume, when the number of holes presumably remains constant, the diffusion coefficient should be nearly independent of temperature. With the second model, the average kinetic energy of the molecules and therefore their ability to surmount the repulsive potential barrier [should] increase with temperature. Also, the greater fluctuation of nearest neighbors increases the probability of finding lower potential barriers to overcome. On this model one would expect an appreciable temperature coefficient of diffusion at constant volume. In the case we have investigated, $(\partial \ln D/\partial T)_P$ at one atmosphere and 25°C is 0.0185, and $(\partial \ln D/\partial T)_V$ is 0.0034. These may be compared with the temperature coefficient of the kinetic energy, which is equal to 0.00335.

Similar conclusions were drawn later by Watts, Alder, and Hildebrand[15] from the self-diffusion of CCl_4. They reported, further, that the experimental activation energy for diffusion, either at constant pressure or at constant volume, when substituted in the diffusion equation based on hole theory, did not give reasonable distances for a molecular jump into an adjacent "hole."

3. *Partial molal volumes of iodine in liquids with "holes" of different size.* The size of holes in a lattice or of dislocations in a mosaic structure should depend upon the sizes of the molecules composing the liquid, provided they are highly symmetrical; molecules of small size, accordingly, should find holes more nearly ready to accommodate them in a solvent with large molecules than in one with small molecules. To test this, Shinoda and Hildebrand[16] determined the magnitude of the partial molal volume of iodine, at high dilution in solvents with molal volumes ranging from 97 cc to 312 cc. Results were obtained for violet solutions as shown in Table 5.2.

Table **5.2.** PARTIAL MOLAL VOLUME OF I_2, $\bar{V}_2$, IN LIQUIDS
OF DIFFERENT MOLAL VOLUMES, V_1^o, cc

Solvent	V_1^o	$\bar{V}_2$
$SiCl_4$	115	67.1
$i\text{-}C_8H_{18}$	166	66.7
$c\text{-}(CH_3)_8Si_4O_4$	312	66.6
CCl_4	97	66.7

The iodine molecules evidently must dig their own "holes"; they do not find in the siloxane holes partly ready to receive them which are three times as large as holes in carbon tetrachloride.

15 H. Watts, B. J. Alder, and J. H. Hildebrand, *ibid.*, **23,** 659 (1955).
16 K. Shinoda and J. H. Hildebrand, *J. Phys. Chem.*, **62,** 295 (1958).

4. *Entropy of vaporization.* The familiar **Trouton rule,** states that the molal heats of vaporization of "normal" liquids divided by their boiling points in °K are approximately 21 cal/mole/deg. It is evident, however, that this quotient increases slowly with temperature, and several investigators have given empirical expressions to represent the increase. In 1915, Hildebrand[17,18] published a substitute that has become known as the **Hildebrand rule.** According to this rule, entropies of vaporization of unassociated liquids are equal, not at their boiling points, but at temperatures at which their vapors occupy equal volumes.

In the vaporization of a pure liquid,

$$\frac{\Delta s^V}{v^g - v^l} = \frac{dP}{dT} \tag{5.2}$$

At temperatures far below the boiling point $v^g \gg v^l$, and v^l can be neglected. If the vapor can be assumed to obey the gas laws,

$$\Delta s^V = R \frac{d \ln P}{d \ln T} \tag{5.3}$$

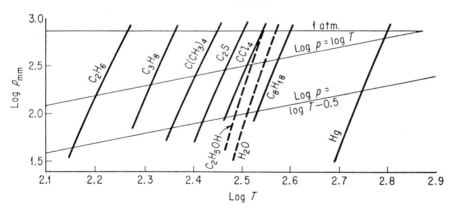

Figure 5.9 Vapor pressures and the "Hildebrand rule."

Figure 5.9 gives a plot of log P vs. log T for a number of liquids. The tangents to these curves have virtually equal slopes at the same vapor volume, not at 1 atmosphere at their boiling points. Ethyl alcohol and water, two strongly associated liquids given for comparison, give steeper curves, corresponding to the extra entropy involved in destroying the association.

[17] J. H. Hildebrand, *J. Am. Chem. Soc.*, **37**, 970 (1915); **40**, 45 (1918).
[18] R. S. Halford, *J. Chem. Phys.*, **8**, 496 (1940); O. L. I. Brown, *J. Am. Chem. Soc.*, **74**, 6096 (1952).

Table **5.3.** ENTROPIES OF VAPORIZATION TO SATURATED VAPOR
VOLUME OF 49.5 liters/mole IN cal/mole/deg

	Eqn. 5.2	Eqn. 5.3
Neopentane	21.8	20.1
Isopentane	22.1	20.2
n-Pentane	22.3	20.7
2,3-Dimethyl butane	. . .	20.3
n-Hexane	22.2	21.5
2,2-Dimethyl hexane	22.0	. . .
n-Octane	22.4	. . .

Table 5.3 gives values of entropy of vaporization to the same vapor
volume of three groups of isomers, the molecules of the liquids within
each group differing in symmetry. The values in the last column were
obtained according to Eqn. 5.2 from large-scale plots of the type shown in
Fig. 5.9. Those in the preceding column were obtained by Hermsen and
Prausnitz,[19] using present knowledge of the gas imperfections of these substances to obtain v^g.

The small increases in Δs^V in going from the more symmetrical to the
less symmetrical isomer have been interpreted as indicating a small degree
of quasi-parallel arrangement among the linear molecules. A similar interpretation was given for the fact that the value of Δs^V at $v^g = 403$ liters for
$n\text{-}C_7F_{16}$, 31.1 cal/deg is larger than the value for $n\text{-}C_7H_{16}$, 29.5 cal/deg. The
molecules for the fluorocarbon are undoubtedly less flexible than those of
the hydrocarbon.[20]

The considerable accuracy of the Hildebrand rule is significant, both
in relation to intermolecular forces, discussed in the next chapter, and in
relation to liquid structure, the topic of this one. *It indicates that all liquids
with fairly symmetrical molecules possess equal amounts of configurational
entropy under the conditions of comparison, a situation quite unlikely to exist
if the molecular disorder in them were less than maximum.*

FREE VOLUME THEORY   The term "free volume"
has been loosely used for three distinguishable concepts.[21] One is the excess
of the volume occupied per mole of substance over the sum of the volumes

[19] R. W. Hermsen and J. M. Prausnitz, *J. Chem. Phys.*, **34**, 108 (1961).
[20] J. H. Hildebrand and G. J. Rotariu, *J. Chem. Phys.*, **74**, 4455 (1952).
[21] Cf. J. H. Hildebrand, *J. Chem. Phys.*, **31**, 1423 (1959).

of all the individual molecules. Another is the excess of the molar volume over the volume at 0°K, determined either from the density of the solid or by extrapolating liquid volume to 0°K. A third is the value of v_f calculated from the entropy of vaporization by means of the equation:

$$\Delta s^V = R \ln \frac{v^g}{v_f} \tag{5.4}$$

These three concepts of free volume have been distinguished[22] by the terms, "empty volume," "expansion volume," and "fluctuation volume," respectively.

Fluctuation volume has been used in theories of the liquid state as a true thermodynamic quantity. It is easy to assume that Eqn. 5.4 is valid because the entropy of expansion of a van der Waals fluid from v to v′ would be

$$R \ln \frac{(v' - b)}{(v - b)}$$

The fact is, however, that a definite functional relation between volume and free volume is implied in any method of evaluating v_f.

The role ascribed to free volume is formally analogous to that of probability in the familiar equation, $S = k \ln \Omega$, as expressed by the relation:

$$\left(\frac{\partial S}{\partial V}\right)_T = \left(\frac{\partial s}{\partial v}\right)_T = R\left(\frac{\partial \ln v_f}{\partial v}\right)_T \tag{5.5}$$

The analogy suffers, however, from the fact that in a liquid there are no naturally discrete states corresponding to energy levels of a quantized system, or to lattice sites of a crystal. The "cells" assumed are metaphysical. Any method of calculating values of v_f from Eqn. 5.5 or any derivative of it is dependent upon the particular assumption concerning liquid structure in order to evaluate $\partial v_f/\partial v$, and different assumptions yield markedly different values, as illustrated in Table 5.4 for two typical

Table 5.4. FREE VOLUMES CALCULATED IN VARIOUS WAYS

	v^o cc	$(\partial S/\partial V)_T$ cal cc⁻¹ deg⁻¹	"Expansion volume" $v - v^o$	"Fluctuation volume" from Eqn. 5.4	From Eqn. 5.6	From Eqn. 5.8
			Free Volume v_f cc			
CCl_4	97	0.271	24	0.24	7.34	0.34
$c\text{-}C_6F_{11}CF_3$	196	0.182	...	0.36	10.9	0.24

[22] A. Bondi, *J. Phys. Chem.*, **58**, 929 (1954).

non-polar liquids, CCl_4 and c-$C_6F_{11}CF_3$. We use the accurate values of $(\partial S/\partial V)_T = (\partial P/\partial T)_V$ that have been measured by Smith and Hildebrand.[23]

In the column headed Eqn. 5.4 are given values of free volume calculated from the entropy of vaporization. It is to be noted that these values are less than 1 cc, although these liquids are greatly expanded over their minimum volumes. The "expansion volume" of CCl_4 is about 24 cc. If free volume in a liquid were of the van der Waals type, valid for a gas, $v_f = v - b$, Eqn. 5.5 would give

$$v_f = \frac{R}{(\partial S/\partial V)_T} \tag{5.6}$$

and the values in the next column of the table. Obviously, a van der Waals type of free volume is not valid for integration over the entire van der Waals path from liquid to vapor.

The very small volumes yielded by Eqn. 5.4 have been envisioned as spherical volumes swept out by the centers of molecules oscillating in fixed "cages." The calculation varies with the precise geometrical details of the model, but may be represented here by a "simplified free volume" which Hirschfelder, Curtiss, and Bird[24] obtained from a cubic quasi-lattice:

$$v_f = 8(v^{1/3} - N_0^{1/3}\,\sigma)^3 \tag{5.7}$$

Using this expression in Eqn. 5.5 gives

$$v_f^{1/3} = \frac{2R}{v^{2/3}(\partial S/\partial V)_T} \tag{5.8}$$

In this equation the essential feature is the dependence of the free volume on the cube of $(\partial S/\partial V)_T$, unlike Eqn. 5.6, although the actual calculation is very sensitive to the choice of the numerical coefficient (in this case, 2). Equation 5.8 leads to the values in the final column of Table 5.4.

It is evident that the "cage" model gives greater consistency between the entropy of vaporization Δs^V and $(\partial S/\partial V)_T$; however, the most detailed free volume theories cannot be made consistent with all the thermodynamic properties of a liquid, although some workers continue to try. Free volume is *not* a physical parameter and cannot be a thermodynamic one. All detailed free volume models of liquids involve basically unrealistic assumptions concerning liquid structure. They are unrealistic because the nearest neighbors of a molecule are not arranged in a geometrical lattice, or in "cells"; the centers of molecules in a pure liquid are not moving in rigid

[23] E. B. Smith and J. H. Hildebrand, *J. Chem. Phys.*, **31**, 145 (1959).

[24] J. O. Hirschfelder, C. F. Curtiss, and R. B. Bird, *Molecular Theory of Gases and Liquids* (John Wiley and Sons, Inc., New York, 1954), p. 280.

cages, tracing the periphery of even approximately spherical volumes; each is, on the contrary, involved with its neighbors in "random walks," as in Brownian movement. There is a *mean* velocity and a *mean* path-length, but no frequency of oscillation; nothing but "noise."

Benninga and Scott[25] measured $(\partial P/\partial T)_V$ for CCl_4 between -7 deg and 70 deg, which enabled them to compare $\partial E/\partial V$ and $\Delta E^V/v$ with predictions of "free volume theory." They stated their conclusions as follows:

There is, however, no agreement at all between the internal pressure functions, and they are decreasing with T and V. The experimental values are slightly greater than the cohesive energy densities, instead of being much smaller, and they are decreasing with T (and V), whereas the theoretical internal pressures are increasing. Consequently the theoretical value of n is entirely wrong. . . .

It is evident that the energy-volume-temperature relations for liquids present a severe and sensitive test for a theory of liquids. The Lennard-Jones and Devonshire "free-volume" or cell model, even as subsequently refined, fails badly here (at least for carbon tetrachloride) as do most other treatments. An adequate theory of liquids must account for the approximate equality ($n \approx 1$) of the internal pressure and the cohesive energy density of a normal liquid over the entire normal liquid range of temperatures.

Dahler and Hirschfelder[26] have made an exhaustive study of the free-volume theory of liquids. They stated their conclusion in these words:

We find that the isotherms derived from this theory resemble continuations of the crystalline isotherms and agree neither with the Monte Carlo nor with the experimental isotherms for liquids. Furthermore, the results of our calculations are not in accord with those obtained by the method of Lennard-Jones and Devonshire. A major factor contributing to this failure of the cell theory is the artificially high degree of order built into the model. Although it has often been supposed that this order could be disrupted by introducing holes or empty cells into the theory, we find that the slight increase of entropy which accompanies the introduction of such a hole is more than offset by the enormous amount of energy required for its production. Therefore, the criterion of the thermodynamical stability based upon the free energy function does not favor a large number of holes. As a consequence of this the introduction of holes will not significantly alter the theoretical estimates for the thermodynamical properties.

An interesting light is being thrown upon liquid structure by Alder and Wainwright,[27] using the "molecular dynamic method" with electronic computers. Dr. Alder has written, in a private communication to the senior author:

[25] H. Benninga and R. L. Scott, *J. Chem. Phys.*, **23**, 1911 (1955).

[26] J. S. Dahler and J. O. Hirschfelder, ibid., **32**, 330 (1960).

[27] B. J. Alder and T. E. Wainwright, "Molecular Dynamics by Electronic Computers," *Transport Properties in Statistical Mechanics* (Interscience Publishers, 1958).

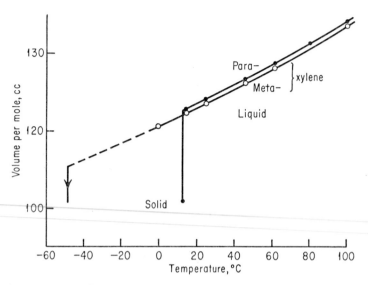

Figure 5.10 Molal volumes and freezing temperatures of meta- and para-xylenes.

Our Molecular Dynamics studies give no support to the lattice concept of the liquid state. As you know, by following the trajectories of the molecules and projecting them on the screen, we can "see" the transitions between the solid and the liquid state. The solid is regularly ordered, with excursions from lattice points taking place, but they are never large enough for the molecules to escape. The transition occurs when such an excursion is simultaneously accompanied by movement of surrounding molecules out of the way. Once this has happened, the whole region becomes disorganized, and subsequently no discernible order is present, and no holes can be observed. The system undergoes random motions, and if one observes it during very few collisions, a molecule remains, of course, surrounded by its neighbors, but never for very long. As the density is decreased, it remains surrounded by the same neighbors during even fewer collisions. Diffusion takes place by a random walk with very small steps, and certainly not by jumping from hole to hole.

The properties of liquid meta- and para-xylenes offer especially striking evidence concerning the hypothesis that liquids contain distinguishable "solid-like" and "gas-like" molecules as postulated by Eyring.[28] In Fig. 5.10 the molal volumes of *m*- and *p*-xylene are plotted against temperature. They were calculated from densities measured by Massart,[29] except the

[28] H. Eyring and Taikue Ree, *Proc. Nat. Acad. Sci.*, **47**, 526 (1961).

[29] L. Massart, *Bull. Soc. Chim. Belg.* **45**, 76 (1916). See Timmermans, *Physico-Chemical Constants of Pure Organic Compounds*, Elsevier Pub. Co., 1950.

point for solid *p*-xylene, which we determined. One sees that the molal volumes are very nearly the same from 100° down to 15°. *M*-xylene is liquid down to −47.9°. *P*-xylene freezes at 13.2°, its volume contracting by 16.8 per cent, but its molal volume shows not the slightest intimation, even at 15°, of the fact that it will freeze at 13.2°. If these isomers contained "solid-like" molecules, the fraction of them present at any one temperature would have to be very different. Their molal heat capacities in the liquid state, published by Pitzer and Scott,[30] are identical within the scatter of the measurements. The assumption that the heat capacity of a liquid is a function of its content of solid-like aggregates seems untenable.[31]

[30] K. S. Pitzer and D. W. Scott, *J. Am. Chem. Soc.*, **65**, 803 (1943).
[31] J. H. Hildebrand and G. Archer, *Proc. Nat. Acad. Sci.*, **47**, 1881 (1961).

CHAPTER 6

Intermolecular Forces

In order to predict the enthalpy of mixing from properties of the pure components, one needs a basis for calculating the excess of the intermolecular potential energies of the components over the same in the mixture, and this, in turn, calls for a relation between the like and unlike pair potential energies, u_{11}, u_{22}, and u_{12}.

The subject of intermolecular forces is difficult and complex. We set forth here only so much of it as is necessary for our purpose. For an extensive exposition, we refer the reader to the monumental work of Hirschfelder, Curtiss, and Bird.[1] An excellent, briefer exposition is to be found in the recent book by Rowlinson.[2]

---

[1] J. O. Hirschfelder, C. F. Curtiss, and R. B. Bird, *Molecular Theory of Gases and Liquids* (John Wiley and Sons, Inc., New York, 1954).

[2] J. S. Rowlinson, *Liquids and Liquid Mixtures* (Butterworth's Scientific Publications, London, 1959).

LONDON FORCES

Since only non-polar molecules may be expected to mix to form regular solutions, we begin by setting forth the pertinent features of intermolecular pair potentials between molecules of this type.

The foundation of the theory of interaction between non-polar molecules was laid by London,[3] in 1930. He explained the nature of this interaction as follows:

Though it is of course not possible to describe this interaction mechanism in terms of our customary classical mechanics, we may still illustrate it in a kind of semi-classical language.

If one were to take an instantaneous photograph of a molecule at any time, one would find various configurations of nuclei and electrons, showing in general dipole moments. In a spherically symmetrical rare gas molecule, as well as in our isotropic oscillators, the average over very many of such snapshots would, of course, give no preference for any direction. These very quickly varying dipoles, represented by the zero-point motion of a molecule, produce an electric field and act upon the polarizability of the other molecule and produce there induced dipoles, which are in phase and in interaction with the instantaneous dipoles producing them. The zero-point motion is, so to speak, accompanied by a synchronized electric alternating field, but not by a radiation field: The energy of the zero-point motion cannot be dissipated by radiation.

Applying this concept, London arrived at the formula

$$u_{12} = -\frac{3\alpha_1\alpha_2}{2r^6} \cdot \frac{h\nu_{0,1} \cdot h\nu_{0,2}}{h\nu_{0,1} + h\nu_{0,2}} \tag{6.1}$$

where ν_0 refers to the frequency characteristic of a molecule in its unperturbed state, corresponding to its "zero-point energy," α denotes polarizability, and r the distance between the centers of two molecules. The perturbation of electronic motion by another molecule is related to its perturbation by light of varying energies (frequencies), as expressed by the formula for the dispersion of light; i.e., the variation of refractive index, n, with frequency, ν, which, for gases, is

$$n - 1 = \frac{C}{\nu_0^2 - \nu^2} \tag{6.2}$$

where C is a characteristic constant. It is this relationship which led London to designate this type of molecular interaction as "dispersion effect."

Values of $h\nu_0$ can be calculated for substances for which the refractive index has been measured over a range of wave lengths. Moreover, $h\nu_0$ is very nearly equal to the ionization energy, **I,** so Eqn. 6.1 can be written

[3] R. Eisenschitz and F. London, *Z. Physik,* **60,** 491 (1930); F. London, ibid., **63,** 245 (1930); *Z. physik. Chem.,* **B11,** 222 (1930); *Trans. Faraday Soc.,* **33,** 8 (1937).

$$u_{12} = -\frac{3}{2} \cdot \frac{\alpha_1 \alpha_2}{r^6} \cdot \frac{I_1 I_2}{I_1 + I_2} \qquad (6.3)$$

If the two molecules are of the same species, Eqns. 6.1 and 6.3 become

$$u_{12} = -\frac{3\alpha^2 h\nu_0}{4r^6} = -\frac{3\alpha^2 I}{4r^6} = -\frac{k}{r^6} \qquad (6.4)$$

The important features of this potential for regular solution theory are: (1) *it is temperature independent*, (2) *it is almost exactly additive, in pairs, non-specific;* (3) *it is short in range;* (4) *its strength depends upon the number and "looseness" of the electrons.*

Although London designated these as "dispersion forces," it is fitting to honor his memory by calling them *London forces,* analogous to the common term, "van der Waals forces." The two are equivalent only for non-polar molecules. The latter term includes all factors involved in deviations from ideal gas behavior: dipoles, hydrogen bonds, and weak complexes.

The model used by London is only an approximation in the case of molecules containing many electrons, where the problem is very complex. A critical review of attempts which have been made to deal with such cases has been published by Pitzer.[4] The attraction potential coefficients, k, calculated by the several methods differ widely from each other and from experimental values. In the case of argon, for example, the experimental value is -109.2 erg cm^6 $\times$ 10^{-16} while three respective theoretical values are -50.3, -64, and -129×10^{-16}. With such uncertainty as to the potential between molecules of the same species, it is evident that we are far from having a reliable theoretical basis for calculating the change in potential energy involved in mixing liquids of different species.

Polarizability and ionization potential are valuable guides for estimating the internal forces of different liquids, but the most direct measurement is afforded by the terms in the thermodynamic equation of state,

$$\left(\frac{\partial E}{\partial V}\right)_T + P = T\left(\frac{\partial P}{\partial T}\right)_V = T\left(\frac{\partial S}{\partial V}\right)_T$$

as outlined later in this chapter and in the next.

POTENTIAL ENERGY CURVES

At small distances, a repulsive potential sets in rather suddenly. It has been variously represented by an exponential formula,

[4] K. S. Pitzer, "Inter- and Intramolecular Forces and Molecular Polarizability," *Advances in Chemical Physics,* Vol. II, p. 59 (Interscience Publishers, Inc., New York, 1959).

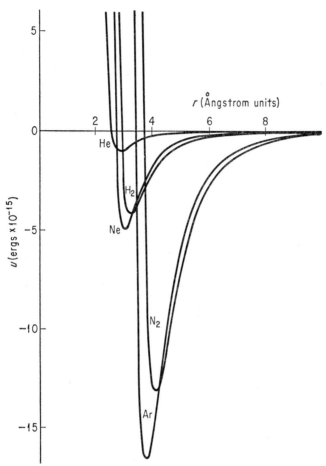

Figure 6.1 Intermolecular pair potentials.

$$u = je^{-cr} \tag{6.5}$$

or by a high inverse power term, first suggested by Mie,[5]

$$u = \frac{j}{r^n} \tag{6.6}$$

Lennard-Jones[6] combined the latter with the London inverse sixth power for attraction in the expression

$$u = \frac{j}{r^n} - \frac{k}{r^6} \tag{6.7}$$

[5] G. Mie, *Ann. Physik.* [4] **11**, 657 (1903).
[6] J. E. Lennard-Jones, *Proc. Roy. Soc.* (London), **A112**, 214 (1926).

with $n = 12$, a choice which makes the equation much simpler to use, and which appears to fit the data for simple molecules fairly well. His plot of u vs. r for five gases is given in Fig. 6.1. The repulsion rises so steeply for the heavier molecules that the error involved in assigning the value $n = 12$ is not very serious. In order to obtain approximate values for k, one may even consider the molecules as hard spheres.

Instead of using the parameters j and k of Eqn. 6.7, one may use σ, the diameter of a molecule; i.e., the distance of closest approach when $u = 0$, and ϵ, the minimum value of u, is considered as an attraction constant and

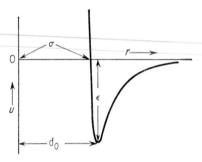

Figure 6.2   The parameters used in expressing intermolecular pair potentials.

taken as a positive quantity. These are illustrated in Fig. 6.2. When $u = 0$, $r = \sigma$, and when $du/dr = 0$, $u = -\epsilon$, and $r^6 = 2\sigma^6$, whence $j = k\sigma^6$ and $k = 4\sigma^6\epsilon$. Substituting these values gives

$$u = 4\epsilon\left[\left(\frac{\sigma}{r}\right)^{12} - \left(\frac{\sigma}{r}\right)^{6}\right] \tag{6.8}$$

As an alternative to expressing u as a function of ϵ and σ, one may use ϵ and d_0, which gives

$$u = \epsilon\left[\left(\frac{d_0}{r}\right)^{12} - 2\left(\frac{d_0}{r}\right)^{6}\right] \tag{6.9}$$

The relation of σ and d_0, consistent with $n = 12$, is $\sigma = d_0/2^{1/6} = 0.8909d_0$.

EVALUATION OF σ AND ϵ_0 FROM SECOND VIRIAL COEFFICIENTS

The parameters σ and ϵ (or d_0 and ϵ) are commonly evaluated from second virial coefficients. Deviations from the behavior of a perfect gas are conveniently expressed by the coefficients in the "virial equation":

$$\frac{P\mathrm{v}}{RT} = 1 + \frac{B(T)}{\mathrm{v}} + \frac{C(T)}{\mathrm{v}^2} + \cdots \tag{6.10}$$

The term $B(T)$ is called the "second virial coefficient." The higher terms can be neglected as a first approximation. Experimental values of $B(T)$ can be used to evaluate intermolecular pair potentials, since

$$B(T) = 2\pi N_0 \int (1 - e^{u/kT}) r^2 dr \tag{6.11}$$

If the potential energy $u(r)$ can be written in a reduced form

$$u(r) = \epsilon f\left(\frac{\sigma}{r}\right)$$

as in Eqn. 6.8, it follows that the second virial coefficient can be expressed in a reduced form as well:

$$B(T) = \sigma^3 \Phi\left(\frac{kT}{\epsilon}\right) \tag{6.12}$$

where the nature of the function Φ depends only on the form of the function $f(\sigma/r)$.

The methods used in evaluating u from $B(T)$ are explained by Hirschfelder, Curtiss, and Bird. These authors express the results by the values of the parameters, σ and ϵ/k, where k is the Boltzmann constant. The values can also be calculated from viscosities.

An interesting discussion of the validity of the "6-12" intermolecular potential used in Eqns. 6.8 and 6.9 occurred during the Discussions of the Faraday Society in 1953 (No. 15, p. 108) among Guggenheim, Rowlinson, and others. We quote remarks by Guggenheim which are still pertinent:

CRITICAL REGION. Lennard-Jones and Devonshire chose the 6-12 interaction for algebraic convenience. The 6-12 interaction which fits the second virial coefficients leads to a satisfactory value for the critical temperature, but to a value for the crystal volume which is too small by a factor of 2.

CRYSTAL. For the crystal and liquid states only values of r near the minimum are relevant. The natural procedure is then to express the interaction energy in the form

$$-\epsilon + \frac{K(r - R)^2}{R^2}$$

where K is a numerical constant. The 6-12 interaction implies that $K = 36$. If one tries to fit the properties of the crystal by the 6-12 interaction appropriate to the second virial coefficients one finds good agreement as regards ϵ, fair agreement as regards R, and no agreement as regards K.

LIQUID. What I have said so far is factual. What I now say about the liquid state is partly a matter of opinion. No treatment of the liquid can seriously be regarded as quantitative unless the values of K as well as those of ϵ and R fit the facts for the crystal. If by suitable choice of the *three* parameters, ϵ, R, K, one can obtain a useful fit for crystal and liquid, I have little doubt that the part of the interaction curve for larger r can be adjusted to give a good fit of second virial coefficients.

Later during the discussion he added this statement:

I said that the second virial coefficient tells us next to nothing about the inter-action energy curve *in the immediate neighborhood of its minimum*, which is the most important part for the solid and liquid states.

Guggenheim and McGlashan[7] made a comprehensive correlation of the interaction between argon atoms with the temperature dependence of the entropy and the density of the crystal, the second virial coefficient of the gas, and the viscosity of the gas at high temperatures. They found that "The interaction energy which best accords with all of these properties is strikingly different from the commonly advocated difference between an inverse twelfth power and an inverse sixth power of the distance."

RELATION BETWEEN PAIR POTENTIAL AND TOTAL LIQUID POTENTIAL ENERGY

We approach our objective of predicting heats of mixing by expressing it in terms of the difference between the potential energy of the solution and that of its pure components.

The potential energy of a pure liquid can be expressed, as shown by Hildebrand and Wood in 1933,[8] in terms of its molecular pair potential and its distribution function, by an integration over all the continuous intermolecular distances in a way analogous to the summation over all lattice sites of the pair potentials in a crystal. The number of molecules in a shell of thickness dr at distance r around any one molecule is (cf. Chapter 5)

$$\frac{N_0}{V} 4\pi g(r) r^2 dr$$

and their potential energy with respect to this molecule is

$$\frac{N_0}{V} 4\pi u(r) g(r) r^2 dr$$

Integrating this over all the molecules in 1 mole of liquid gives for its total potential energy:

$$E = \frac{2\pi N_0^2}{V} \int u(r) g(r) r^2 dr \qquad (6.13)$$

[7] E. A. Guggenheim and M. L. McGlashan, *Proc. Roy. Soc.*, (London), **225**, 456 (1960).

[8] J. H. Hildebrand and S. E. Wood, *J. Chem. Phys.*, **1**, 817 (1933).

(The 4 becomes 2 in order not to count each pair twice, once when the first molecule is regarded as central, once when the second is central.)

If u is expressed by Eqn. 6.6, Eqn. 6.13 becomes

$$\mathrm{E} = \frac{2\pi N_0^2}{\mathrm{V}} \left[\mathrm{j} \int \frac{\mathrm{g}(r)}{r^{n-2}} \, dr - \mathrm{k} \int \frac{\mathrm{g}(r)}{r^4} \right] dr \qquad (6.14)$$

Hildebrand, Wakeham, and Boyd[9] evaluated k, j, and n for mercury by setting $\mathrm{E} = -\Delta\mathrm{E}^\mathrm{V}$, the energy of vaporization, and using their values for $\mathrm{g}(r)$ determined over a considerable range of temperature. They obtained the values (ergs, Ångstroms)

$$k = 3.52 \times 10^{-10}, \quad j = 5.49 \times 10^{-8}, \quad n = 9$$

This value of k is remarkably close to one calculated from the London formula, Eqn. 6.4. Using the ionization potential, $\mathbf{I} = 10.38$ electron-volts and $\alpha = 5.2 \times 10^{-24}$ cc calculated from the refractive index of mercury vapor measured by Wolfsohn,[10] one obtains

$$k = 3.35 \times 10^{-10}$$

The more accurate measurements by Campbell and Hildebrand of scattering by mercury using monochromatic x-rays have been treated somewhat differently by Kerr and Lund,[11] who found

$$k = 3.35 \times 10^{-10}, \quad j = 2.95 \times 10^{-8}, \quad n = 8.3$$

For liquid argon, they found

$$k = 1.02 \times 10^{-10}, \quad j = 2.09 \times 10^{-8}, \quad n = 10.4$$

Moelwyn-Hughes[12] has calculated these parameters from the compressibility of liquid mercury, obtaining the value $n = 9$, with somewhat different values for j and k. Epstein and his co-workers[13] have compared the parameters obtained from x-ray scattering with those obtained from the viscosity of the vapor. The agreement is fairly good. Hirschfelder, Curtiss, and Bird give values of ϵ/k obtained by both methods.

[9] J. H. Hildebrand, H. R. R. Wakeham, and R. N. Boyd, *J. Chem. Phys.*, **7**, 959, 1094 (1939).

[10] G. Wolfsohn, *Z. Physik*, **63**, 634 (1930); **83**, 234 (1933).

[11] R. H. Kerr and L. H. Lund, *J. Chem. Phys.*, **19**, 50 (1951).

[12] E. A. Moelwyn-Hughes, *J. Phys. Coll. Chem.*, **55**, 1246 (1951). See also *Physical Chemistry* (Pergamon Press, London, New York, Paris, 1957).

[13] L. F. Epstein and M. D. Powers, *J. Phys. Chem.*, **57**, 336 (1953); J. S. Lukesh, W. H. Howland, L. F. Epstein, and M. D. Powers, *J. Chem. Phys.*, **23**, 1923 (1955).

POTENTIAL ENERGY BETWEEN POLYATOMIC MOLECULES

The attractive energy between polyatomic molecules arises predominantly from interaction between adjacent portions of their electron clouds, and, therefore, decreases with increasing separation more rapidly than the inverse sixth power of separation of their centers. Repulsion also is highly dependent upon molecular geometry and the bending and stretching characteristics of bonds.

Kihara[14] has assumed that the Lennard-Jones potential is exerted between cores inside the molecule. He gives the expression:

$$u = \epsilon \left[\left(\frac{\rho_0}{\rho} \right)^{12} - 2 \left(\frac{\rho_0}{\rho} \right)^{6} \right] \tag{6.15}$$

where ρ is the shortest distance between cores and ρ_0 its value at the potential minimum. For spherical cores of radius a at distance r between molecular centers, $\rho = r - 2a$.

Another approach to forces between "quasi-spherical" polyatomic molecules, such as CF_4, SF_6, P_4, etc., is that developed by Hamann and Lambert.[15] They considered the interaction between two molecules with their principal centers of attraction (peripheral atoms) distributed throughout a spherical shell at a distance a from the geometrical center and integrated over the whole volume, assuming a Lennard-Jones potential between individual elements. For the simple case that a is one half the van der Waals radius of the molecule, the resulting potential energy function is fitted remarkably well by a Lennard-Jones type of potential with exponents 7 and 28. The net effect, as in the Kihara core potential, is to make the attractive energy a mildly steeper function of r and the repulsive energy a much steeper function. Figure 6.3 illustrates the Hamman 7-28 potential and the Kihara core potential for two cases ($r_0 = 4a$, $\rho_0 = 2a$; and $r_0 = 5a$, $\rho_0 = 3a$), as compared with the simple Lennard-Jones 6-12 potential; in the region of practical importance for liquids, the 7-28 potential and the Kihara potential for a core $r_0 = 5a$ are almost indistinguishable.

EVIDENCE FROM ENTROPY OF VAPORIZATION

One line of evidence is afforded by the entropy of vaporization. Pitzer[16] pointed out that the theory of corresponding states leads to equal entropies of vaporization at equal ratios of gas to liquid volumes. The necessary conditions are "(1) the

[14] T. Kihara, *Rev. Mod. Phys.*, **25**, 831 (1953).

[15] S. D. Hamman and J. A. Lambert, *Austr. J. Chem.*, **7**, 1 (1954).

[16] K. S. Pitzer, *J. Chem. Phys.*, **7**, 583 (1939).

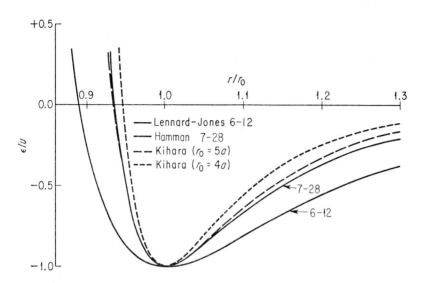

Figure 6.3 Intermolecular potential energies for polyatomic molecules.

validity of classical statistical mechanics, (2) spherical or freely rotating molecules, (3) intermolecular vibration the same in liquid and gas, (4) potential energy depending only on intermolecular distances, and (5) universal shape of potential curves." He showed that argon, krypton and xenon have the entropies of vaporization: 18.67, 18.60, 18.66 cal/deg mole respectively when compared at $v^g/v^l = 335$, but when they are compared at equal gas volumes, in accordance with the Hildebrand rule described in Chapter 5, their respective entropies of vaporization are 19.0, 18.5, 18.0 cal/deg mole.

Guggenheim[17] extended Pitzer's treatment to other properties, and in discussing vaporization wrote, "Neither Trouton's rule nor Hildebrand's accords with the principle of corresponding states, which requires, rather, that the molar entropies of evaporation should be equal at corresponding temperatures." It has been apparent, nevertheless, that, as stated by Halford,[18] "This definition of characteristic temperature [i.e., that derived from corresponding states] cannot compete in practical value with the empirical rule of Hildebrand," and Frank,[19] after examining many cases, wrote on the same point, "This [Eyring's assumption that the product of

[17] E. A. Guggenheim, *J. Chem. Phys.*, **13**, 253 (1945).

[18] R. S. Halford, *J. Chem. Phys.*, **8**, 496 (1940).

[19] H. S. Frank, ibid., **13**, 493 (1945).

compressibility with molal volume is constant] does not do justice to the rule, however, for it is far more accurate than such a statement would imply."

Hildebrand[20] suggested, in 1937, that it might prove realistic, in the case of certain polyatomic molecules such as those of the tetrahalides, to consider the outer atoms as the main centers of attraction. The range of the London forces is so short that the more remote atoms contribute but little to the total effect. Such molecules do not satisfy Pitzer's conditions 4 and 5 and, therefore, would not be expected to conform to the principle of corresponding states.

Hildebrand and Gilman[21] compared values of the entropy of vaporization of two closely similar pairs of liquids,

$$\text{(a)} \quad Cl_2 \quad \text{and} \quad CCl_4$$

$$\text{(b)} \quad C_2H_6 \quad \text{and} \quad (CH_3)_2CHCH(CH_3)_2$$

(1) at equal vapor volumes, (2) at equal ratios of vapor to liquid, and (3) at equal reduced temperatures. Their results were, in part, as follows:

Entropy of vaporization of:	v^g	v^g/v^l	T/T_c
Cl_2 at 223°K is 22.6; CCl_4 at same...............	22.1	24.2	26.4
C_2H_6 at 148°K is 25.8; $(CH_3)_2CHCH(CH_3)_2$ at same	25.5	28.3	. . .

The molal volume of the larger species is 2.3 times that of the smaller in the case of the first pair, and 2.5 times that of the smaller in the second, As expected, these systems do not follow the law of corresponding states.

PITZER'S ACENTRIC FACTORS

Pitzer and his co-workers[22] showed that these models are all consistent with an extended theory of corresponding states in which a third parameter expresses the effect of a finite core size regardless of the shape of the core. This third parameter, which they named the "acentric factor," was defined empirically by the equation

$$\omega = -\log\left(\frac{P}{P_c}\right) - 1.000$$

where P is the vapor pressure at a reduced temperature 0.70 and P_c is the

[20] J. H. Hildebrand, *Trans. Faraday Soc.*, **33**, 144 (1937).

[21] J. H. Hildebrand and T. S. Gilman, *J. Chem. Phys.*, **15**, 229 (1947).

[22] K. S. Pitzer, D. Z. Lippmann, R. F. Curl, Jr., C. M. Huggins, and D. E. Petersen, *J. Am. Chem. Soc.*, **77**, 3427, 3433 (1955); **79**, 2369 (1957); *Ind. Eng. Chem.*, **50**, 265 (1958).

critical pressure. In effect, ω measures the extra entropy of vaporization above that expected for a simple (earlier called perfect) fluid exemplified by Ar, Kr, or Xe. Substances having equal acentric factors may be expected to show the same agreement with the theory of corresponding states. Volumetric data on various normal fluids were found to conform to this theory, but water and ammonia showed deviations. Values of the acentric factor ω for a number of liquids are given in Appendix 2.

EVIDENCE FROM EXPANSION AND VAPORIZATION

Another line of evidence that intermolecular potential energies are acentric is furnished by the departures of polyatomic liquids from the behavior of a van der Waals liquid, for which

$$\left(\frac{\partial E}{\partial V}\right)_T = \frac{a}{v^2}$$

as may be seen by comparing the van der Waals equation with the "thermodynamic equation of state," as follows:

$$P + \frac{a}{v^2} = \frac{R}{v - b}$$

$$P + \left(\frac{\partial E}{\partial V}\right)_T = T\left(\frac{\partial P}{\partial T}\right)_V \tag{6.16}$$

Smith and Hildebrand[23] determined $\partial P/\partial T$ for five liquids with molal volumes ranging from 120 to 230 cc. In the case of $c\text{-}C_6F_{11}CF_3$, for example, a rather compact molecule, $v^2(\partial E/\partial V)$ diminished from 21.1 to 20.4 $\times$ 10^5 (cal cc moles^{-2}) between 13.5 deg and 41.3 deg. Benninga and Scott[24] found a smaller but definite decrease in the case of CCl_4.

If $\partial E/\partial V = a/v^2$, then the potential energy of a liquid with respect to its dilute vapor is $E = -a/v$. Setting $E = \Delta E^V$ gives[25] $a = v\,\Delta E^V$. But a in this way also decreases with increasing v. It is possible to correlate these drifts by writing $E = -a/v^n$, as suggested by Frank.[26] This gives

[23] E. B. Smith and J. H. Hildebrand, *J. Chem. Phys.*, **31**, 145 (1959).

[24] H. Benninga and R. L. Scott, ibid., **23**, 1911 (1955).

[25] J. H. Hildebrand, *Phys. Rev.*, **34**, 984 (1929). Also, J. H. Hildebrand and R. L. Scott, *Solubility of Nonelectrolytes* (Reinhold Publishing Corporation, New York, 1950), p. 97.

[26] H. S. Frank, *J. Chem. Phys.*, **13**, 495 (1945).

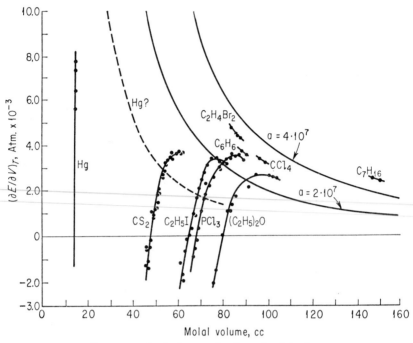

Figure 6.4 $(\partial E/\partial v)_T$ *as a function of molal volume.*

$$v^{n+1}\left(\frac{\partial E}{\partial V}\right) = nv^n\,\Delta E^V = \text{const.} \tag{6.17}$$

Hildebrand,[27] in 1939, explained the decrease in $v\,\Delta E^V$ in terms of Eqn. 6.13. If it is written

$$v\,\Delta E = 2\pi N_0^2 \int u(r)g(r)r^2 dr \tag{6.18}$$

the right-hand member is the van der Waals a. It decreases slowly with rising temperature because of the slow lowering and simultaneous broadening of the first and main peak of the distribution function, illustrated in Fig. 5.5.

Values of $n > 1$ are confirmed both by the decrease with rising temperature of both functions $v\,\Delta E^V$ and $v^2(\partial E/\partial V)$, and by values of $n > 1$ in the term $nv^n\,\Delta E^V$, as illustrated in Table 6.1, from the paper by Smith and Hildebrand.[22] The original value of 1.09 for CCl_4 was confirmed by Benninga and Scott.

One sees clearly that the values of n in Table 6.1 increase more rapidly

[27] J. H. Hildebrand, *J. Chem. Phys.*, **7**, 1 (1939); **15**, 727 (1947).

with increasing v the more complex the molecule, and the more acentric its force field.

A relation such as Eqn. 6.17 can not be valid for low temperatures or high pressures, where repulsion plays a major role, as illustrated in Fig. 6.4.

A striking example of an acentric force field is afforded by cyclo-octamethyl-tetrasiloxane, c-$(CH_3)_8Si_4O_4$. The central, octagonal core of alternating silicon and oxygen atoms is so buried under eight methyl groups that the liquid dissolves iodine with a pure violet color. Its solubility relations, as we shall see in later chapters, place it close to cyclohexane in solvent power (see Fig. 9.1) instead of to fluorocarbons, as would be expected if its potential field were central.

Table 6.1. VALUES OF n IN EQUATION 6.17

	$(\partial E/\partial V)_T$ cal/cc	ΔE^V cal	n
C_7F_{16}	51.3	7.76	1.49
c-$C_6F_{11}CF_3$	54.4	7.34	1.44
n-C_6F_{14}			1.39*
c-$C_4Cl_2F_6$	62.2	6.55	1.35
n-$C_4Cl_3F_7$	65.1	7.92	1.36
$CCl_2F \cdot CClF_2$	62.6	6.33	1.19
CCl_4	81.0	7.20	1.09
n-C_6H_{14}			1.09*

* R. D. Dunlap and R. L. Scott, *J. Phys. Chem.*, to be published.

POTENTIAL ENERGIES BETWEEN UNLIKE MOLECULES

The relation between the van der Waals constant[28] for a mole of a binary mixture and the constants for its pure components is

$$a = x_1^2 a_1 + 2x_1 x_2 a_{12} + x_2^2 a_2 \qquad (6.19)$$

where a_{12} represents the interaction between the unlike molecular species, and the x's represent the mole fractions. Berthelot[29] proposed the relation

$$a_{12} = (a_1 a_2)^{1/2} \qquad (6.20)$$

Introduction of Eqn. 6.20 into 6.19 makes it a perfect square:

$$a = (x_1 a_1^{1/2} + x_2 a_2^{1/2})^2 \qquad (6.21)$$

The London equations for the potentials between like and unlike

[28] J. D. van der Waals, *Z. physik. Chem.*, **5**, 133 (1890).
[29] D. Berthelot, *Comptes Rendu*, **126**, 1703, 1857 (1898).

molecules, Eqns. 6.3 and 6.4, at equal values of the intermolecular distance, r, yield the relation

$$u_{12} = \frac{2(I_1 I_2)^{1/2}}{I_1 + I_2} (u_1 u_2)^{1/2} \qquad (6.22)$$

Since geometric means are less than arithmetic means, unlikeness in intermolecular potentials of the components of a mixture leads to a weakening of cohesion. We shall see that this results, in general, in increases in volume and enthalpy upon mixing, with increases over ideal vapor pressures and decreases from ideal solubilities. These effects should be expected even for molecules with acentric potentials, provided always that there are no specific, "chemical" interactions, such as association, or complex formation.

A rather severe test of the Berthelot relation, Eqn. 6.20, was made by Hildebrand and Carter[30] with liquid mixtures of tetrahalides. From measurements of $(\partial P/\partial T)_V$ for the pure liquids and their solutions, they calculated $(\partial E/\partial V)_T$ and a van der Waals a $= v^2(\partial E/\partial V)_T$. They found that values of a for mixtures at $x_1 = x_2 = 0.5$ agreed within 1 per cent with values calculated from values of a_1 and a_2 by Eqn. 6.21, as seen in Table 6.2.

Table 6.2. TEST OF THE BERTHELOT RELATION
FOR TETRAHALIDE LIQUID MIXTURES

	a in atm liter²				
	Pure components		Values a for solutions at $x = 0.5$		
	v, cc	a, obs.	obs.	Eqn. 6.21	$(a_1 + a_2)/2$
CCl₄	97.09	31.21	46.86	46.46	48.00
SnBr₄	130.62	64.79	48.69	48.17	49.40
SiCl₄	115.36	34.00	43.28	43.14	44.28
SiBr₄	126.52	53.56			

It is instructive to observe that the values of a observed, and the closely agreeing values calculated by Eqn. 6.21, are less than the arithmetical means of a_1 and a_2. These differences represent the weakening of the internal forces resulting in expansion, heat absorption, increased escaping tendencies, and solubilities less than ideal. However, the disparity is of the order of only 3 per cent. The difficulty facing any theory of solubility is the fact that it must deal with small differences between large quantities.

Among other confirmations of the geometric mean between unlike simple molecules is one obtained from the scattering of He and Ar in each other by Amdur, Mason, and Harkins.[31] Further consideration of the potential energy between unlike molecules is given in Chapters 8–10.

[30] J. H. Hildebrand and J. M. Carter, *J. Am. Chem. Soc.*, **54**, 3592 (1932).
[31] I. Amdur, E. A. Mason, and A. L. Harkins, *J. Chem. Phys.*, **22**, 107 (1954).

ASSOCIATED LIQUIDS

Association of one compo-
nent of a mixture, as through hydrogen bonds, tends to make $u_{12} < (u_1u_2)^{1/2}$,
while complexing tends to make $u_{12} > (u_1u_2)^{1/2}$. Equal hydrogen bond
strength between the like and unlike molecules, e.g., ethyl and propyl
alcohols, may permit $u_{12} \cong (u_1u_2)^{1/2}$. Alcohols give cyclic or linear polymers
of indefinite length; water gives three-dimensional, indefinite complexes
whose structure is related to that of ice.

Molecules with permanent, but not hydrogen-bonding, dipoles super-
impose an electrostatic attraction upon the ever present London forces.
In the most favorable orientation, the potential between two dipoles (not
between the centers of the molecules in which they are situated) is
$u = -2\mu_1\mu_2/r^3$, where μ denotes dipole moment. But thermal agitation
interferes with this orientation, and dipolar attraction diminishes with
rising temperature. At intermediate temperatures, attractive orientations
are statistically preferred, and Keesom,[32] applying Boltzmann statistics,
derived for the average potential the expression:

$$u = -\frac{2}{3} \cdot \frac{\mu_1^2\mu_2^2}{r^6 kT} \tag{6.23}$$

This expression is strictly valid only for point dipoles imbedded in otherwise spherically symmetric molecules. The analysis becomes much more
complicated for non-spherical molecules and for dipoles as they are actually
located. From the form of this equation, it is evident that the dipole interaction between relatively weak, somewhat buried dipoles, such as $CHCl_3$,
$\mu = 0.95$ debye units, and ether, $\mu = 0.99$, does not add very much to the
London potential.

MOLECULES WITH ASYMMETRIC FIELDS OF FORCE

Smith, Walkley, and Hilde-
brand[33] made certain determinations of partial molal volumes of bromine
that furnish information about the effect of asymmetric molecular fields of
force. These results are represented in Fig. 6.5, where the partial molal
volume of bromine is plotted against the volume fraction of CCl_4, (1) in
mixtures of C_7F_{16} and CCl_4, (2) in mixtures of $c\text{-}C_4Cl_2F_6$ and CCl_4. One sees
from the line for the first mixture that the effect of CCl_4 in decreasing the
partial molal volume of bromine is much more than additive. It is evident
that when CCl_4 is present in appreciable mole fraction the Br_2 molecules
are able to establish contact preferentially with molecules of CCl_4.

---

[32] W. H. Keesom, *Physik. Z.*, **22**, 126, 643 (1921); **23**, 225 (1922).
[33] E. B. Smith, J. Walkley, and J. H. Hildebrand, *J. Phys. Chem.*, **63**, 703 (1959).

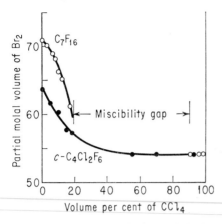

Figure 6.5 Partial molal volume of Br_2 in mixtures with CCl_4.

In the case of pure c-$C_4Cl_2F_6$, the F-atoms, although smaller than Cl-atoms, are three times as numerous, so the added Br_2 cannot at first surround itself exclusively with the latter; however, it succeeds in doing so long before CCl_4 occupies half of the volume of the mixture.

These observations show that one may expect more or less ambivalence in the case of molecules whose parts differ appreciably in the strength of their fields of force. For example, one might expect a substance such as $CCl_3 \cdot CF_3$ to approach CCl_4 as a solvent for iodine, and also to mix rather well with a pure fluorocarbon. This sort of ambivalence doubtless accounts for the extraordinary versatility of ethers and ketones as solvents.

ELECTRON DONOR-ACCEPTOR INTERACTION

In 1923, Lewis[34] generalized the acid-base concept to include, as acids, not only protons, but any substance able to "accept," without activation energy, a "lone pair" of electrons from another molecule, designated a base. Typical acids, under this definition, include I_2, ICl, $SnCl_4$, Al_2Br_6, SO_2, CO_2, BCl_3, BF_3. Typical bases include ketones, ethers, aromatics, olefins, ammonia, alkyl iodides and sulfides. Weiss,[35] in 1942, called attention to the relation of complexing to the electron affinity of acids and ionization potential of bases.

Benesi and Hildebrand,[36] in 1948, discovered the intense ultraviolet absorption in solutions of iodine in benzene, toluene, o- and p-xylene, mesitylene, benzotrifluoride, and ether, shown in part in Fig. 6.6. They reported the wave lengths and extinction coefficients of both the ultraviolet and visible bands. From the effects upon the ultraviolet bands of changing the concentrations of iodine and aromatic in a non-complexing

[34] G. N. Lewis, *Valence and the Structure of Atoms and Molecules* (Chem. Catalog Co., New York, 1923). See also "Acids and Bases," *J. Franklin Inst.*, **226**, 293 (1938).

[35] J. Weiss, *J. Chem. Soc.*, 245 (1942).

[36] H. A. Benesi and J. H. Hildebrand, *J. Am. Chem. Soc.*, **70**, 2832 (1948); **71**, 2703 (1949).

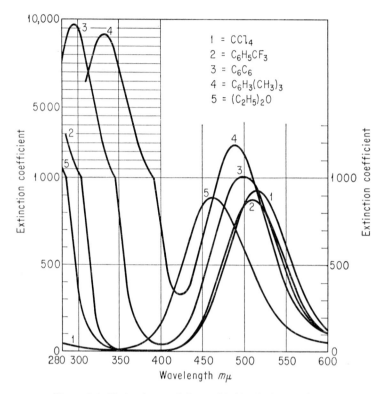

Figure 6.6   Extinction coefficients of iodine in donor solvents.

solvent, the equilibrium constants for 1:1 complexes were determined, as shown in Table 6.3.

Freed and Sancier[37] made a similar study of the brown complex between

Table 6.3. EQUILIBRIUM CONSTANTS FOR IODINE
COMPLEXES WITH AROMATICS

Solvent	Aromatic	K
CCl_4	C_6H_6	1.72
CCl_4	$1,3,5-(CH_3)_3C_6H_3$	7.2
C_7H_{16}	C_6H_6	1.15
C_7H_{16}	$1,3,5-(CH_3)_3C_6H_3$	5.3

[37] S. Freed and K. M. Sancier, *J. Am. Chem. Soc.*, **74**, 1273 (1952).

iodine and propylene in propane, stable at liquid nitrogen temperatures.

The discovery of this new measure of electron donor-acceptor interaction led to widespread use of this means of investigation. Most notable have been the series of papers by Mulliken[38] and his collaborators, who have developed a theory of "charge-transfer complexes."

McConnell, Ham, and Platt[39] published a straight-line plot of the intensity of the charge-transfer transition vs. wave length for benzene with a series of acceptor molecules increasing in the following order:

$$(COCl)_2, \quad SO_2, \quad C_6H_3(NO_2)_3, \quad Cl_2O, \quad ICl, \quad Br_2, \quad I_2$$

They gave also the plot, reproduced in Fig. 6.7, of the relation between the

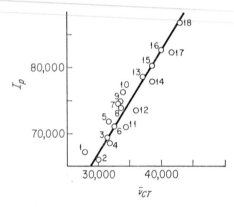

Figure 6.7   Ionization potential of the donor molecule versus the frequency of the charge-transfer transition maximum of its complex with iodine: 1. naphthalene, 2. mesitylene, 3. o-xylene, 4. p-xylene, 5. 2-methylbutadiene, 6. toluene, 7. cyclohexene, 8. transbutene-2, 9. benzene, 10. cisbutene-2, 11. chlorobenzene, 12. butadiene, 13. propene, 14. cisdichloroethylene, 15. transdichloroethylene, 16. diethyl ether, 17. cyclopropane, 18. t-butyl alcohol.

ionization potential of base molecules and the frequency of the charge-transfer transition maximum of its complex with iodine.

Walkley, Glew, and Hildebrand[40] reinvestigated the shift of the visible band of iodine in donor solvents and found that they fall into two distinct groups when their ionization potentials are plotted against wave lengths

[38] R. S. Mulliken, *J. Am. Chem. Soc.*, **70**, 600 (1950); **74**, 811 (1952); *J. Phys. Chem.*, **56**, 801 (1952).

[39] H. McConnell, J. S. Ham, and J. R. Platt, *J. Chem. Phys.*, **21**, 66 (1953).

[40] J. Walkley, D. N. Glew, and J. H. Hildebrand, *J. Phys. Chem.*, **33**, 621 (1960).

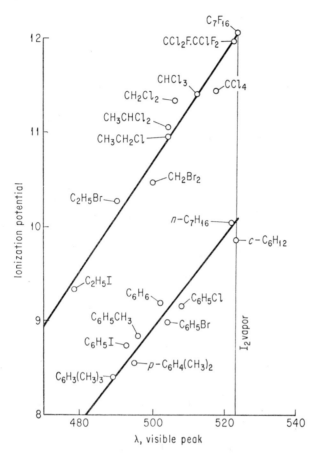

Figure 6.8 Wavelength of the visible absorption peaks of iodine in donor solvents.

of the peaks, as seen in Fig. 6.8. The complexes are formed with the N-electrons (non-bonding) of solvents of one group, with the π-electrons of the other. The data are given in Table 6.4.

It thus becomes evident that interaction between molecules of different species may depart from the geometric mean for reasons other than those expressed by a Kihara potential. It seems likely that the potentials between unlike molecules will have to take account not only of the magnitude and shape of the potentials between molecules of the same species, but also of the nature of their electron clouds. The two groups of iodine solutions and the divergent behavior of hydrogen, evident in Chapter 4, suggest that three kinds of electrons should be differentiated: N-electrons,

Table 6.4. WAVE LENGTHS OF VISIBLE ABSORPTION PEAKS
OF IODINE IN SOLUTION AND IONIZATION POTENTIALS
OF THE SOLVENTS

N-Donors	λ (mμ)	I (e.v.)
C_7F_{16}	523	12.08
CCl_2FCClF_2	522	11.99
CS_2	518	. . .
CCl_4	517	11.47
$CHCl_3$	512	11.42
CH_2Cl_2	506	11.35
CH_3CHCl_2	504	11.07
CH_3CH_2Cl	504	10.97
CH_2Br_2	500	10.48
CH_2ClCH_2Cl	497	11.08
CH_2BrCH_2Br	496	. . .
C_2H_5Br	490	10.29
C_2H_5I	478	9.33

π-Donors	λ (mμ)	I (e.v.)
C_6H_6	502	9.24
C_6H_5Cl	498	. . .
$C_6H_5CH_3$	496	8.82
p-$(CH_3)_2C_6H_4$	495	8.55
C_6H_5I	493	8.73
$1,3,5$-$(CH_3)_3C_6H_3$	489	8.39

π-electrons and bonding electrons. Evidences of this distinction will be cited in subsequent chapters. It suggests at least a partial explanation of the failure of the binary solutions of benzene, cyclohexane, and carbon tetrachloride, which were investigated with great precision by Scatchard, Wood, Mochel, Austin, and Brusie,[41] to give a triangle of additive relations. A striking evidence of attraction between benzene and carbon tetrachloride in excess of that attributable to London forces alone is to be seen in the freezing out of a 1:1 compound with a heat of dissociation of 3.5 kcal/mole, discovered by Goates, Sullivan, and Ott.[42] Non-additive, specific interactions such as these are evidently far more numerous than formerly suspected, because, unlike iodine solutions, there is in most cases

[41] G. Scatchard, S. E. Wood, and J. M. Mochel, *J. Phys. Chem.*, **43**, 119 (1939); *J. Am. Chem. Soc.*, **61**, 3206 (1939). S. E. Wood and J. P. Brusie, *J. Am. Chem. Soc.*, **65**, 1891 (1943). S. E. Wood and A. E. Austin, ibid., **67**, 480 (1945).

[42] J. R. Goates, R. J. Sullivan, and J. B. Ott, *J. Phys. Chem.*, **63**, 589 (1959).

no color change to reveal their presence. Their existence should serve to warn against the pitfalls of oversimplification; they reveal a complexity, but add thereby to the fascination of the work of building a valid theory of solutions.

CHAPTER 7

Heat of Mixing

BACKGROUND

The first attempt to treat the changes in entropy or enthalpy when two liquids are mixed was made in 1906 by van Laar,[1] who based his work upon the van der Waals equation of state. Van der Waals[2] had already given equations for the constants a and b in gas mixtures:

$$a = x_1^2 a_1 + 2x_1 x_2 a_{12} + x_2^2 a_2 \qquad (7.1a)$$

$$b = x_1 b_1 + x_2 b_2 \qquad (7.1b)$$

Equation 7.1a allows for the attractions between three kinds of molecular pairs: 1-1, 1-2, and 2-2; Eqn. 7.1b is a kind of volume additivity assumption. With these and the van der Waals equation for energy, $E = -a/v$, one can write

---

[1] J. J. van Laar, *Sechs Vorträge über das thermodynamische Potential* (Braunschweis, 1906); *Z. physik. Chem.*, **72**, 723 (1910); *Z. physik. Chem.*, **83**, 599 (1913).

[2] J. D. van der Waals, *Z. physik. Chem.*, **5**, 133 (1890).

$$\Delta_E{}^M = E_m - x_1 E_1 - x_2 E_2 = -\frac{a}{V_m} + x_1 \frac{a_1}{V_1} + x_2 \frac{a_2}{V_2} \qquad (7.2)$$

If there is no volume change on mixing, and if the liquids are essentially unexpanded (i.e., if $v = b$), $\Delta_E{}^M = \Delta_H{}^M$ and van Laar could write

$$\Delta_H{}^M = \Delta_E{}^M = \frac{x_1 x_2}{x_1 b_1 + x_2 b_2} (a_1 b_2^2 - 2 a_{12} b_1 b_2 + a_2 b_1^2) \qquad (7.3)$$

Van Laar also assumed that the interaction constant a_{12} satisfies the Berthelot relation[3]

$$a_{12} = (a_1 a_2)^{1/2} \qquad (7.4)$$

and simplified Eqn. 7.3 further to

$$\Delta_H{}^M = \frac{x_1 x_2 b_1 b_2}{x_1 b_1 + x_2 b_2} \left(\frac{a_1^{1/2}}{b_1} - \frac{a_2^{1/2}}{b_2} \right)^2 \qquad (7.5)$$

According to this expression, the heat of mixing is never negative and can be zero only if $a_1^{1/2}/b_1 = a_2^{1/2}/b_2$, which, as van Laar pointed out, is the case if the two components have equal critical pressures, since, according to the van der Waals equation, $P_c = a/27b^2$.

The corresponding partial molal enthalpies can be obtained by appropriate differentiation, and van Laar then equated

$$RT \ln \gamma_1 = RT \ln \left(\frac{p_1}{p_1^o x_1} \right)$$

to Δ_{H_1}. However, he expressed his equation for partial vapor pressure, not with the above variables, but with

$$r = \frac{b_2 - b_1}{b_1} \quad \text{and} \quad \beta = \frac{(b_2 a_1^{1/2} - b_1 a_2^{1/2})^2}{RT b_1^3}$$

$$\ln \frac{p_1}{p_1^o x_1} = \frac{\beta x_2^2}{(1 + r x_2)^2}, \quad \ln \frac{p_2}{p_2^o x_2} = \frac{\beta x_1^2}{(1 + r)(1 + r x_2)^2} \qquad (7.6)$$

This pair of equations has often been used, by adjusting the parameters β and r, to fit experimental data, and to apply the Gibbs-Duhem equation. They are not reliable, however, for predicting the behavior of solutions, because of the inadequacy of the basic van der Waals equation to cover the whole range from 1 atmosphere to the critical point. Cl_2 and CCl_4, for example, form a practically ideal solution, although their critical pressures are 76 and 45 atmospheres, respectively. Again, CS_2 and CH_3OH are so unlike as to form two liquid phases, although their critical pressures are nearly the same—76 and 79 atmospheres. Van Laar did not recognize the role of polarity until much later. A theoretician, he was content to give a few illustrations showing qualitative agreement only. His thermo-

[3] D. Berthelot, *Comptes rendus*, **126**, 1703, 1857 (1898).

dynamics was better than most of that current in the early days of physical chemistry, but he entangled it almost inextricably with the inadequate van der Waals equation, and he wrote in a fashion better calculated to make enemies than friends.

In 1925, van Laar and Lorenz[4] improved Eqn. 7.3 by substituting actual molal volumes for the b's; i.e.,

$$\Delta_H{}^M = \frac{x_1 v_1 x_2 v_2}{(x_1 v_1 + x_2 v_2)} \left(\frac{a_1^{1/2}}{v_1} - \frac{a_2^{1/2}}{v_2} \right)^2 \tag{7.7}$$

Dolezalek,[5] in 1908, attempted to account for non-ideal solutions by assuming chemical equilibria, either association or solvation or both, with all the "true" molecular species obeying Raoult's law. Van Laar[1] violently attacked this hypothesis and developed further his point of view that differences in van der Waals forces suffice to explain non-ideal behavior. Solvation may, of course, be described as equivalent to the assumption that the solvent-solute interaction constant a_{12} is greater than the geometric mean $(a_{11}a_{22})^{1/2}$ of the Berthelot relation; indeed, it would be safer to restrict "chemical" interpretations to cases in which a_{12} is decidedly greater than even the arithmetic mean $(a_{11} + a_{22})/2$.

In 1916, Hildebrand[6] published the first of a series of papers on solubility in which he discussed the contentions of van Laar, Dolezalek, and others. He pointed out that Dolezalek has assumed association in liquids which according to all other evidence are quite normal; that no reasonable type of association could account for the formation of two liquid phases; that polarity could play a major role; and that the order of solubility of a given solute in a series of solvents is determined by relative internal pressures, except for disturbances due to polarity. In 1919,[7] he gave various methods for obtaining the relative internal pressures, including the energy of vaporization per unit volume, $\Delta_E{}^V/v$, the "cohesive energy density," which has become the quantity most useful for calculating deviations from ideal solutions.

THE SCATCHARD-HILDEBRAND EQUATION

In 1931, Scatchard[8] published an important paper which, in his own words, "may be regarded also as a quantitative development of the treatment of Hildebrand, although it

[4] J. J. van Laar and R. Lorenz, *Z. anorg. allgem. Chem.*, **146**, 42 (1925).

[5] F. Dolezalek, *Z. physik. Chem.*, **64**, 727 (1908).

[6] J. H. Hildebrand, *J. Am. Chem. Soc.*, **38**, 1452 (1916).

[7] J. H. Hildebrand, *J. Am. Chem. Soc.*, **41**, 1067 (1919).

[8] G. Scatchard, *Chem. Rev.*, **8**, 321 (1931). See also *Kemisk Maanensblad*, **13**, 77 (Copenhagen, 1932); *J. Am. Chem. Soc.*, **56**, 995 (1934); *Trans. Faraday Soc.*, **33**, 160 (1937).

disagrees with his ideas in some important details, or as a method of freeing the van Laar treatment from the inadequacies of the van der Waals equation." His basic assumptions were as follows: (1) the mutual energy of two molecules depends only upon the distance between them and their relative orientation, and not at all on the nature of the other molecules between or around them or on the temperature; (2) the distribution of the molecules in position and in orientation is random; i.e., it is independent of the temperature and of the nature of the other molecules present; (3) the change of volume on mixing at constant pressure is zero.

These assumptions permit writing the "cohesive energy" of a mole of liquid mixture:

$$-E_m = \frac{c_{11}v_1^2 x_1^2 + 2c_{12}v_1 v_2 x_1 x_2 + c_{22}v_2^2 x_2^2}{x_1 v_1 + x_2 v_2}$$

For the pure components $-E = c_{11}v_1$, etc.; therefore, c_{11} is $-E_1/v_1$, or the "cohesive energy density." For liquids at ordinary temperatures, the vapor is nearly ideal, so we can identify $-E$ with the energy of vaporization, ΔE^V, and write $c_{11} = \Delta E_1^V/v_1$.

Transforming to volume fractions ϕ_1 and ϕ_2, we obtain

$$-E_m = (x_1 v_1 + x_2 v_2)(c_{11}\phi_1^2 + 2c_{12}\phi_1\phi_2 + c_{22}\phi_2^2)$$

From this Scatchard obtained for the energy of mixing

$$\Delta E^M = E_m - E_1 x_1 - E_2 x_2 = (x_1 v_1 + x_2 v_2)(c_{11} + c_{22} - 2c_{12})\phi_1\phi_2$$
$$= (x_1 v_1 + x_2 v_2)A_{12}\phi_1\phi_2 \tag{7.8}$$

where $A_{12} = (c_{11} + c_{22} - 2c_{12})$. If we further assume that $c_{12} = (c_{11}c_{22})^{1/2}$, Scatchard's fourth assumption, A_{12} may be written

$$A_{12} = (c_{11}^{1/2} - c_{22}^{1/2})^2 \tag{7.9}$$

These square roots of the cohesive energy densities assume such an important role in the theory of solutions that we have called them **solubility parameters** and have designated them by a special symbol, δ. In our notation, we may write Scatchard's equation as

$$\Delta E^M = (x_1 v_1 + x_2 v_2)\left[\left(\frac{\Delta E_1^V}{v_1}\right)^{1/2} - \left(\frac{\Delta E_2^V}{v_2}\right)^{1/2}\right]^2 \phi_1\phi_2$$
$$= (x_1 v_1 + x_2 v_2)(\delta_1 - \delta_2)^2 \phi_1\phi_2 \tag{7.10}$$

This is identical with Eqn. 7.7 of van Laar and Lorenz if the van der Waals a in the latter equation is defined as $v \Delta E^V$.

The same equation was derived by Hildebrand and Wood[9] in 1933 by integrating the intermolecular potential energies between pairs throughout the liquid by aid of the continuous radial distribution functions. A revised

[9] J. H. Hildebrand and S. E. Wood, *J. Chem. Phys.*, **1**, 817 (1933).

version of the derivation was given later;[10] we merely summarize the argument here.

As explained in Chapter 5, in a pure liquid of spherically symmetric molecules, a spherical shell of radius r around a designated central molecule, and thickness dr will contain $(N/V)4\pi r^2\, g(r)\, dr$ molecules where $g(r)$ is the radial distribution function. The potential energy of a pure liquid of N molecules in volume V is then

$$E = \frac{2\pi N^2}{V}\int_0^\infty u(r)g(r)r^2 dr = n\,\frac{2\pi N_0^2}{\mathrm{v}}\int_0^\infty u(r)g(r)r^2 dr \qquad (7.11)$$

where $u(r)$ is the potential energy of a pair of molecules separated by distance r, as discussed in Chapter 6.

In a solution, around a central molecule of component 1, molecules of both 1 and 2 may be found, and the probability of finding a type 1 molecule is proportional to $(N_1/V)\, g_{11}(r)$ whereas that of finding a type 2 molecule is proportional to $(N_2/V)\, g_{21}(r)$. Similar relations hold for molecules around a central type 2 molecule, and since the probabilities that the central molecule is 1 or 2 are respectively x_1 and x_2, we may write for the potential energy of the mixture in a volume

$$V_m = n_1\mathrm{v}_1 + n_2\mathrm{v}_2 = (n_1 + n_2)(x_1\mathrm{v}_1 + x_2\mathrm{v}_2)$$

$$E_m = \frac{(n_1 + n_2)2\pi N_0^2}{x_1\mathrm{v}_1 + x_2\mathrm{v}_2}\left[x_1\left(x_1\int u_{11}g_{11}r^2 dr + x_2\int u_{21}g_{21}r^2 dr\right)\right.$$
$$\left. + x_2\left(x_1\int u_{12}g_{12}r^2 dr + x_2\int u_{22}g_{22}r^2 dr\right)\right]$$

However, since $u_{12} = u_{21}$ and $g_{12} = g_{21}$, one may further simplify and write in a volume fraction form

$$E_m = (n_1\mathrm{v}_1 + n_2\mathrm{v}_2)2\pi N_0^2\left(\frac{\phi_1^2}{\mathrm{v}_1^2}\int u_{11}g_{11}r^2 dr\right.$$
$$\left. + \frac{2\phi_1\phi_2}{\mathrm{v}_1\mathrm{v}_2}\int u_{12}g_{12}r^2 dr + \frac{\phi_2^2}{\mathrm{v}_2^2}\int u_{22}g_{22}r^2 dr\right)$$

The reason for using volume fractions becomes apparent if we write the energy of the unmixed components[11] as

$$E_1 + E_2 = (n_1\mathrm{v}_1 + n_2\mathrm{v}_2)2\pi N_0^2\left(\frac{\phi_1}{\mathrm{v}_1^2}\int u_{11}g_{11}^0 r^2 dr + \frac{\phi_2}{\mathrm{v}_2^2}\int u_{22}g_{22}^0 r^2 dr\right)$$

where g_{11}^0 and g_{22}^0 are the distribution functions for the pure liquids. When

[10] J. H. Hildebrand and R. L. Scott, *Solubility of Nonelectrolytes*, 3rd ed. (Reinhold Publishing Corporation, New York, 1950), pp. 124–129.

[11] We shall see later in this chapter that, unless the volume change on mixing at constant pressure is zero, we must adjust the pressure on either the unmixed components or on the resultant mixture to make $\Delta v = 0$.

this expression for $E_1 + E_2$ is subtracted from the energy of the mixture, we obtain

$$\Delta E^{\mathrm{M}} = E_m - E_1 - E_2 = (n_1 \mathrm{v}_1 + n_2 \mathrm{v}_2) 2\pi N_0^2 \left[\frac{\phi_1^2}{\mathrm{v}_1^2} \int u_{11}(g_{11} - g_{11}^o) r^2 dr \right.$$

$$+ \frac{\phi_2^2}{\mathrm{v}_2^2} \int u_{22}(g_{22} - g_{22}^o) r^2 dr + \phi_1 \phi_2 \left(\frac{2}{\mathrm{v}_1 \mathrm{v}_2} \int u_{12} g_{12} r^2 dr \right.$$

$$\left. - \frac{1}{\mathrm{v}_1^2} \int u_{11} g_{11}^o r^2 dr - \frac{1}{\mathrm{v}_2^2} \int u_{22} g_{22}^o r^2 dr \right) \right] \qquad (7.12)$$

As written, Eqn. 7.12 is exact, if the process is a constant volume one and if the potential energy functions are really spherically symmetric, as we have assumed. To proceed further, we must make some additional assumptions, which are surely approximate at best. For components whose molecules are of the same inherent size and which have the same degree of expansion, we may set $\mathrm{v}_1 = \mathrm{v}_2$ and $g_{11}^o = g_{22}^o$, in accordance with the ideas discussed in Chapter 5. If the distribution of molecules throughout the solution is truly random (i.e., if there is no preferential selection of nearest neighbor pairs) then we may set $g_{11} = g_{12} = g_{22}$ and independent of mole fraction. If all the g's are the same, Eqn. 7.12 reduces for 1 mole of mixture to

$$\Delta_{\mathrm{E}}^{\mathrm{M}} = \frac{2\pi N_0^2}{\mathrm{v}} x_1 x_2 \int (2u_{12} - u_{11} - u_{22}) g r^2 dr = B x_1 x_2 \qquad (7.13)$$

However, although solutions of two components of equivalent molecular size and shape offer convenient simplifications for the theoretician (as, for example, in the "strictly regular solution" or "simple mixture"), they are rarely encountered in the laboratory, and we must seek a way of handling molecules of differing sizes. In the 1933 paper[9] and again in the 1950 book,[10] this was done by invoking the observation that the distribution functions for different species can be superimposed when compared at equal degrees of expansion by plotting g(r) vs. $r/r_{\max}$ where $r_{\max}$ is the distance to the first maximum. (See Chapter 5, Figs. 4 and 6.)

We may equally well write g as a function of r/σ or r/d_0, where σ is the collision diameter and d_0 is the distance of minimum energy, since these are surely proportional to $r_{\max}$ if the substances have similar potential energy functions. We therefore assume three energy functions

$$u_{11} = \epsilon_{11} \, \mathrm{f}\left(\frac{r}{\sigma_{11}}\right), \qquad u_{12} = \epsilon_{12} \, \mathrm{f}\left(\frac{r}{\sigma_{12}}\right), \qquad u_{22} = \epsilon_{22} \, \mathrm{f}\left(\frac{r}{\sigma_{22}}\right) \qquad (7.14)$$

and three radial distribution functions, each independent of the composition (i.e., independent of the variables x or ϕ).

$$g_{11}^o(r) = g_{11}(r) = g\left(\frac{r}{\sigma_{11}}\right), \qquad g_{12} = g\left(\frac{r}{\sigma_{12}}\right), \qquad g_{22}^o(r) = g_{22}(r) = g\left(\frac{r}{\sigma_{22}}\right) \qquad (7.15)$$

If we substitute from Eqns. 7.14 and 7.15 into Eqn. 7.12, and let $y = r/\sigma$, we obtain

$$\Delta E^M = (x_1 v_1 + x_2 v_2)\phi_1\phi_2 \left(\frac{2\epsilon_{12}\sigma_{12}^3}{v_1 v_2} - \frac{\epsilon_{11}\sigma_{11}^3}{v_1^2} - \frac{\epsilon_{22}\sigma_{22}^3}{v_2^2}\right)$$

$$2\pi N_0^2 \int_0^\infty f(y)g(y)y^2 dy \qquad (7.16)$$

Equation 7.16 is obviously equivalent to Scatchard's equation 7.8, with the c's identified as

$$\frac{\epsilon\sigma^3}{v^2} 2\pi N_0^2 \int f(y)g(y)y^2 dy$$

with the further identification (cf. Eqn. 7.11) of c_{11} as $-E_1/v_1$ and c_{22} as $-E_2/v_2$. Equations 7.15 are obviously a mathematical statement of Scatchard's assumption (2) of random distribution, independent "of the nature of the other molecules present."

However, for large differences between the σ's, it is obvious that the assumption of Eqn. 7.15 must be a poor approximation indeed. The extreme example of a dilute solute (2) of large spheres in a solvent (1) of small spheres illustrates this point (Fig. 7.1). The first maximum in g_{12} will be

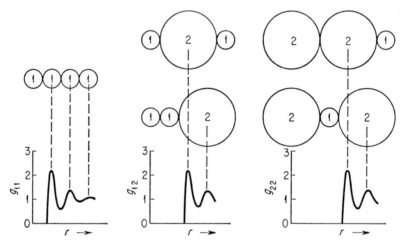

Figure 7.1 Radial distribution functions (schematic) for a dilute solution of large spheres in small spheres.

proportional to σ_{12}, but the second maximum (second shell) will *not* be at $2\sigma_{12}$, but rather at $\sigma_{12} + \sigma_{11}$, because in the dilute solution the intermediate molecules are sure to be the small ones. Similar considerations apply to g_{22}.

We have collected in Table 7.1 some recent calorimetric determinations of the heat of mixing. The last two columns compare the mole fraction (of component 2) x_{max} at which ΔH^M has a maximum with that predicted from Eqn. 7.10.

$$x_{max} = \frac{v_1^{1/2}}{v_1^{1/2} + v_2^{1/2}} \qquad (7.17)$$

Strongly orienting interactions (such as strong hydrogen bonds) have been excluded from Table 7.1. We would not expect a system like ethanol + benzene to fit Eqn. 7.10.

Table **7.1.** COMPOSITION DEPENDENCE OF HEATS OF MIXING

System	$T°$K	v_1/cc	v_2/cc	$\Delta H^M_{max,}$ cal/mole	x_{max} obs	calc
n-hexane + cyclohexane	293	132	109	53[a]	0.60	0.53
n-hexane + n-hexadecane	293	132	294	30[b]	0.48	0.40
iso-octane + n-hexadecane	293	166	294	55[c]	0.42	0.43
perfluoro-n-hexane + n-hexane	298	205	131	516[d]	0.52	0.55
perfluoro-n-heptane + iso-octane	298	205	166	508[d]	0.51	0.53
benzene + n-hexane	293	89	132	208[a]	0.45	0.45
benzene + cyclohexane	298	89	109	182[e]	0.50	0.47
benzene + n-heptane	293	89	147	233[f]	0.45	0.44
toluene + n-heptane	293	107	147	133[a]	0.50	0.46
carbon tetrachloride + cyclohexane	298	97	109	40[e]	0.47	0.48
carbon tetrachloride + methyliodide	298	97	63	67[g]	0.45	0.55
carbon tetrachloride + silicon tetrachloride	298	97	115	32[h]	0.60	0.47
acetone + carbon disulfide	288	73	60	336[i]	0.51	0.53
carbon monoxide + methane	91	37.3	35.5	26[j]	0.60	0.51

[a] A. R. Mathieson and J. C. J. Thynne, *J. Chem. Soc.*, 3708 (1956).

[b] M. L. McGlashan and K. W. Morcom, *Trans. Faraday Soc.*, **57**, 581 (1961).

[c] J. H. van der Waals and J. J. Hermans, *Rec. trav. chim. Pays-Bas*, **69**, 949, 971 (1950).

[d] A. G. Williamson and R. L. Scott, *J. Phys. Chem.*, **65**, 275 (1961).

[e] J. R. Goates, R. J. Sullivan, and J. B. Ott, *J. Phys. Chem.*, **63**, 589 (1959).

[f] C. P. Brown, A. R. Mathieson, and J. C. J. Thynne, *J. Chem. Soc.*, 4141 (1955).

[g] E. A. Moelwyn-Hughes and R. W. Missen, *Trans. Faraday Soc.*, **53**, 607 (1957).

[h] R. D. Vold, *J. Am. Chem. Soc.*, **59**, 1515 (1937).

[i] G. C. Schmidt, *Z. physik. Chem.*, **121**, 221 (1926).

[j] V. Mathot, L. A. K. Staveley, J. A. Young, and N. G. Parsonage, *Trans. Faraday Soc.*, **52**, 1488 (1956).

Actually the data in Table 7.1 give no support to the idea that a volume fraction equation would be better than the mole fraction equation 7.13

(which predicts a symmetrical curve with $x_{max} = 0.50$); the fit is about equally good for both. A better comparison for such a zero[th] approximation would be to confine one's attention to systems with large ΔH's and large differences in molal volumes and to convert to constant volume. Moreover, as we shall see later, Eqn. 7.10 is a better expression for the excess free energy than for the heat of mixing at constant pressure, and it is free energy data (solubility, vapor pressures, etc.) which provide the strongest support for the volume fraction formulation.

Very recently, McGlashan, Morcom, and Williamson[12] have compared their measurements on n-hexane + n-hexadecane with a lattice theory which predicts excess functions which have essentially the volume fraction dependence discussed above. Despite the large differences in molar volume between the two hydrocarbons, the heat of mixing ($H^E = \Delta H^M$) at constant pressure is essentially symmetrical when plotted against mole fraction x (as indicated in Table 7.1). However, when their measurements are converted to a constant volume frame of reference, which is more consistent with theory, the energy of mixing at constant volume ΔE_V^M shows a maximum near $x = 0.4$, in agreement with the prediction of Eqn. 7.17 (Table 7.1).

Anticipating the evidence in subsequent chapters, especially Chapter 10, for the superiority of the volume fraction approach, we suggest that this is due to a combination of factors:

a) The short-range nature of the intermolecular potential energy of a pair of non-polar molecules (attractive energy proportional to r^{-6}) means that the contribution of non-nearest-neighbor molecules to the total energy is small; where our assumptions about $g(r)$ fail, $u(r)$ is so small that the contribution to the integral in Eqn. 7.16 is unimportant.

b) Most of the systems studied do not contain spherical molecules, so the molal volumes are not good measures of the distances σ of closest approach, but more often an approximate measure of the number of interacting units in a more-or-less linear hydrocarbon-like chain.

When differences in molal volumes represent differences in diameters of spherical molecules, we would expect Eqn. 7.16 to fail badly because of the failure of our assumption concerning the distribution functions. Approximately spherical molecules radically different in diameter are very hard to find and rarely coexist as liquids in the same temperature range. The extreme examples shown in Fig. 7.1 were chosen to illustrate the nature of the assumptions and should not be taken too seriously. It is worth noting that a ratio $v_2^o/v_1^o = 2$ corresponds to a difference of only 27% in the diameters of spherical molecules.

[12] M. L. McGlashan, K. W. Morcom, and A. G. Williamson, *Trans. Faraday Soc.*, **57**, 601 (1961).

In fact, if the intermolecular energies are really short range in relation to the dimensions of molecules, we would expect a random distribution to lead to an energy of mixing dependent upon surface areas and "surface fractions"; Langmuir[13] suggested such an approach for molecules with heterogeneous surfaces, but the "surface fraction" approach has not been used much to handle size and shape effects with non-polar materials.

For chain molecules, with a more or less constant diameter to the chain (e.g., methylene-CH_2-units), the surface is, except for end effects, proportional to volume. This doubtless accounts for the success of the volume-fraction formulation in many cases. It will also account for the failure of the volume fraction approach for mixtures of hydrocarbons with fluoro-carbons; in the system $n\text{-}C_6H_{14} + n\text{-}C_6F_{14}$ (Table 7.1), the molal volumes are very different (131 and 205 cm^3, respectively), but the chain length is essentially the same, so it is not surprising that this system is more sym-metrical in mole fraction than is predicted by Eqn. 7.17. Further evidence of the superiority of volume fraction equations over mole fraction equations is presented in Chapter 10.

THE GEOMETRIC MEAN ASSUMPTION

We turn now to the magni-tude of the interaction constant A_{12} in Eqns. 7.8 and 7.16, to consider the reliability of the Berthelot relation, Eqn. 7.9. If we assume v_1 and v_2 are proportional to σ_1^3 and σ_2^3, an assumption correct for liquids of spherical molecules if they are at the same degree of expansion over that of the hy-pothetical liquid at $0°K$ (but of uncertain validity for polyatomic molecules of varying shapes), we may combine Eqn. 7.16 with Eqn. 7.8 and write

$$c_{12}^2 = (c_{11}c_{22}) \frac{\epsilon_{12}^2 \sigma_{12}^6}{\epsilon_{11}\epsilon_{22}\sigma_{11}^3\sigma_{22}^3} \tag{7.18}$$

Since, for dispersion, attractive energy ϵ_{ij} is proportional to

$$\frac{\alpha_i\alpha_j I_i I_j}{(I_i + I_j)\sigma_{ij}^6}$$

we may use this and the further usual assumption that $\sigma_{ij} = (\sigma_{ii} + \sigma_{jj})/2$ to obtain

$$c_{12}^2 = c_{11}c_{22} \frac{I_1 I_2}{\left(\dfrac{I_1 + I_2}{2}\right)^2} \frac{\sigma_{11}^3\sigma_{22}^3}{\left(\dfrac{\sigma_{11} + \sigma_{22}}{2}\right)^6} \tag{7.19}$$

Only if the ionization potentials I_1 and I_2 are equal and also if the colli-sion diameters σ_{11} and σ_{22} are equal can c_{12} be the geometric mean of c_{11} and c_{22}. Accordingly, while the term c_{12} in this equation includes the geo-metric mean of the polarizabilities, it contains the harmonic means of the

[13] I. Langmuir, *Colloid Symposium, Monograph III*, Chemical Catalog Co., New York, 1925, p. 48.

ionization potentials and the molecular diameters. Since these are invariably less than geometric means, we can write

$$c_{12} \leqq (c_{11}c_{22})^{1/2}$$

Normally the polarizabilities of two substances differ by much more than do their ionization potentials, so this complication has been conveniently ignored. However, Reed,[14] in an attempt to account for the large excess free energies of hydrocarbon + fluorocarbon systems, has recently re-emphasized the role of differences in ionization potentials. If we express A_{12} in terms of the solubility parameters δ, we obtain

$$A_{12} = c_{11} - 2c_{12} + c_{22} = (\delta_1 - \delta_2)^2 + 2\delta_1\delta_2(1 - f_I f_\sigma) \qquad (7.20)$$

where

$$f_I = \frac{2I_1^{1/2}I_2^{1/2}}{I_1 + I_2} \quad \text{and} \quad f_\sigma = \left(\frac{2\sigma_{11}^{1/2}\sigma_{22}^{1/2}}{\sigma_{11} + \sigma_{22}}\right)^3$$

Reed estimates that for fluorocarbon + hydrocarbon mixtures f_I is about 0.97 and f_σ about 0.995. For $\delta_1 = 7.5$, $\delta_2 = 6.0$; this makes the second term about 3 cal cm^{-3}, which, when coupled with molar volumes from 100 to 200 cm^3, can produce an energy of mixing at constant volume as much as 150 cal mole^{-1} in excess of that predicted by Eqn. 7.10.

For many substances, however, the ionization potentials are not known. Kohler[15] has suggested an ingenious method for evading this difficulty. If the dispersion attractive energy ϵ is proportional to $\alpha^2 I/\sigma^6$, this may be inverted to express a proportionality between I and $\epsilon\sigma^6/\alpha^2$, or, since c is proportional to ϵ/σ^3, a proportionality between I and $c\sigma^3/\alpha^2$. If this is substituted into Eqn. 7.19, we eliminate the ionization potentials and obtain an expression involving the better-known polarizabilities α instead:

$$\frac{c_{12}^2}{c_{11}c_{22}} = \frac{4\dfrac{c_{11}\sigma_{11}^3 c_{22}\sigma_{22}^3}{\alpha_1^2\alpha_2^2}}{\left(\dfrac{c_{11}\sigma_{11}^3}{\alpha_1^2} + \dfrac{c_{22}\sigma_{22}^3}{\alpha_2^2}\right)^2}\frac{64\,\sigma_{11}^3\sigma_{22}^3}{(\sigma_{11} + \sigma_{22})^6}$$

Munn[16] has applied this procedure to fluorocarbon and hydrocarbon mixtures, using, however, the inappropriate cell model of Prigogine and Bellemans, rather than the equations presented here.

There seems to be no legitimate reason for disregarding ionization potential differences (see Table 7.2), yet that which offers a reasonably satisfactory explanation for the anomalously large heats of mixing and excess free energies of fluorocarbon + hydrocarbon mixtures would pre-

[14] T. M. Reed, III, *J. Am. Chem. Soc.*, **59**, 429 (1955).

[15] F. Kohler, *Monatsh.* **88**, 857 (1957).

[16] R. J. Munn, *Trans. Faraday Soc.*, **57**, 187 (1961).

dict for other solutions similar anomalies which are not found. For example, carbon tetrachloride and iodine (Table 7.2) have ionization potentials as low or lower than aliphatic hydrocarbons, but their mixtures with fluorocarbons show excess free energies in good agreement with Eqn. 7.10 with no need for the correction terms of Eqn. 7.20.

Table 7.2. IONIZATION POTENTIALS FOR
SELECTED SUBSTANCES (in ev)

SF$_6$	19.3	CCl$_4$	11.0
CF$_4$	17.8	n-C$_7$H$_{16}$	10.4
Kr	14.0	I$_2$	9.7
CH$_4$	13.1	C$_6$H$_6$	9.2

95511

As we have seen in Chapter 6 (Eqn. 6.12), the second virial coefficient can yield useful information concerning the parameters ϵ and σ in the Lennard-Jones potential energy expression. Moreover, for gas mixtures, the second virial coefficient depends upon three separate coefficients, each depending upon the parameters of the appropriate pair potential:

$$B_m = x_1^2 B_{11} + 2x_1 x_2 B_{12} + x_2^2 B_{22} \qquad (7.21)$$

When all the potential energy functions are of the same functional form, it can be shown[17,18] that the second virial coefficient can be expressed in a different reduced form using the critical constants for the liquid T^c and V^c and a universal function $g(T^c/T)$

$$B = \text{v}^c g\left(\frac{T^c}{T}\right) \qquad (7.22)$$

The critical constants T^c and v^c are directly proportional to the parameters ϵ and σ^3 respectively, so if

$$\epsilon_{12} = (\epsilon_{11}\epsilon_{22})^{1/2} \quad \text{and} \quad \sigma_{12} = \frac{\sigma_{11} + \sigma_{22}}{2}$$

then one can express B_{12} in terms of fictitious critical constants

$$T_{12}^c = (T_{11}^c T_{22}^c)^{1/2} \quad \text{and} \quad \text{v}_{12}^c = \frac{[(\text{v}_{11}^c)^{1/3} + (\text{v}_{22}^c)^{1/3}]^3}{8}$$

Guggenheim and McGlashan[18,19] have applied these combining rules to the experimental data on a number of mixtures of simple gases

[17] J. H. Hildebrand and R. L. Scott, *op. cit.*, Chapter 14.

[18] E. A. Guggenheim and M. L. McGlashan, *Proc. Roy. Soc.*, (London), **A206**, 448 (1951).

[19] E. A. Guggenheim, *Mixtures* (Oxford University Press, 1952), Chapter 8.

(e.g., $N_2 + O_2$, $Ar + H_2$, $CH_4 + C_2H_6$, etc.) and find that for these systems the observed B_{12} and the experimental B_{12} almost always agree within 2 cm^3 mole^{-1}. These data are frequently cited as justification for the Berthelot geometric mean assumption (Eqn. 7.4 or its equivalent).

However, for many systems involving **polyatomic molecules,** these combining rules as might be expected, are not successful. Hamann, Lambert, and Thomas[20] have made careful measurements of second virial coefficients in the systems methane + neopentane and methane + sulfur hexafluoride, and they find that B_{12} is consistently higher (algebraically) than values estimated from the Guggenheim-McGlashan rules. This they attribute to a failure of the geometric mean assumption for ϵ_{12}; they suggest that ϵ_{12} for the interaction between a monatomic molecule (or a hydride like CH_4 which follows the same law of corresponding states as the inert gases Ar and Kr) and a "quasi-spherical" molecule like CCl_4 or $C(CH_3)_4$ should be less than $(\epsilon_{11}\epsilon_{22})^{1/2}$.

It is clearly an oversimplification to assume an intermolecular potential energy function that is actually appropriate only for monatomic substances. For polyatomic substances the peripheral atoms (such as the chlorines in CCl_4 or the methyls in neopentane) are certainly more nearly the principal centers of attraction than is the geometric center of the molecules. We have seen in Chapter 6 how the Kihara core potential, the Pitzer acentric factor, and the Hamann 7-28 potential have been introduced in an attempt to make more adequate allowance for these complications.

Hamann, Lambert and Thomas[20] have made an ingenious calculation of the interaction between a monatomic molecule and a "quasi-spherical" polyatomic one. They imagine a tetrahedral molecule, AA_4, with five atoms held together at the distance of minimum energy. Then, using a Lennard-Jones 6-12 potential for a monatomic substance (i.e., Eqn. 6.8), they calculate $u(r)$ for the $A + AA_4$ and $AA_4 + AA_4$ interactions by summing over all the A-A pairs in each case. If these functions $u_{12}(r)$ and $u_{22}(r)$ are fitted as nearly as possible to the 6-12 potential, one can obtain constants σ_{12} and σ_{22}, ϵ_{12} and ϵ_{22}. As shown in Table 7.3, σ_{12} is indeed very nearly $(\sigma_{11} + \sigma_{22})/2$, but ϵ_{12} is appreciably less than $(\epsilon_{11}\epsilon_{22})^{1/2}$.

Scott[21] has suggested that this idea might be extended to the interaction between parallel fluorocarbon and hydrocarbon chains. The intermolecular potential function will be centered on the carbon skeleton of the hydrocarbon, but in the fluorocarbon the peripheral fluorine atoms obviously contribute heavily. This, together with the ionization potential, might

[20] S. D. Hamann, J. A. Lambert, and R. B. Thomas, *Austr. J. Chem.*, **8**, 149 (1955).
[21] R. L. Scott, *J. Phys. Chem.*, **62**, 136 (1958).

Table **7.3**

Interaction		ϵ/ϵ_{11}	σ/σ_{11}
$A + A$	(1-1)	1.000	1.000
$AA_4 + AA_4$	(2-2)	2.64	1.74
$A + AA_4$	(1-2)	1.53	1.375

$$(\epsilon_{11}\epsilon_{22})^{1/2} = 1.62\epsilon_{11}, \qquad (\sigma_{11} + \sigma_{22})/2 = 1.37\sigma_{12}$$

account for the anomalies in fluorocarbon + hydrocarbon systems. However, as Scott has pointed out, this interpretation would demand a difference between the behavior of straight-chain hydrocarbons (pseudo-monatomic, like methane) and branched hydrocarbons (like neopentane); no significant differences (particularly in mixtures with fluorocarbons) have been observed.

Considering the narrowness of the theoretical and experimental basis for the geometric mean assumption, it is surprising that it has proved so widely useful, especially in the form of solubility parameter theory, in estimating thermodynamic behavior in solutions.

HEATS OF MIXING AT CONSTANT VOLUME

The usual experimental measurements upon solutions yield values of the thermodynamic functions for mixing at constant pressure, not the energy at constant volume, as discussed in the foregoing pages. Experimental values of the heat of mixing are normally obtained in one of two ways: (1) from the temperature dependence of the excess free energy, derived from vapor pressure measurements at a series of temperatures, and (2) from direct calorimetric measurements upon the mixing process. While vapor pressure measurements have long been a standard source for free energy data, they have frequently yielded unreliable heats of mixing. The uncertainty in these vapor-pressure-derived ΔH's arises from two sources: the small temperature range, which requires taking the small difference between large numbers; and the necessity of making corrections for gas imperfections, corrections which are much larger (because of the higher vapor pressures) at the higher temperatures. Consequently, in recent years, workers[22-25] have been turning

[22] G. H. Cheesman and A. M. B. Whitaker, *Proc. Roy. Soc.*, **A212,** 406 (London, 1952).
[23] D. S. Adcock and M. L. McGlashan, *Proc. Roy. Soc.*, **A226,** 266 (London, 1954).
[24] I. Brown and W. Fock, *Austr. J. Chem.*, **8,** 361 (1955).
[25] A. G. Williamson and R. L. Scott, *J. Phys. Chem.*, **64,** 440 (1960).

to calorimetric measurement of heats of mixing in calorimeters of improved design which eliminate vapor space and permit the use of small quantities of liquid.

The combination of calorimetric data on heats of mixing, preferably at several temperatures, with vapor pressure data can lead to determination of all the excess properties H^E, S^E, and F^E with remarkably high precision.[26]

The conversion of the heat of mixing at constant pressure to the energy of mixing at constant volume is straightforward, and is analogous to the entropy correction in Chapter 3 (further details will be found in Chapter 8):

$$\Delta H_P^M - \Delta E_V^M = H^E - E_V^E = T\left(\frac{\partial P}{\partial T}\right)_V \Delta V_P^M + \ldots \tag{7.23}$$

If $(\partial P/\partial T)_V = \alpha/\beta$ is known for the mixture (or can be estimated from the pure components) and if the volume change ΔV_P^M is known, ΔE_V^M can easily be calculated.

THE EXCESS FREE ENERGY

We are now prepared to combine the heat of mixing and the excess entropy at constant pressure to yield the excess free energy. This can be done, but because of the essential identity of the Helmholtz free energy of mixing at constant volume and the Gibbs free energy of mixing at constant pressure (Chapter 3, Eqn. 3.7; see also Chapter 8), we may equally well combine the excess entropy and energy for the constant volume process. But the former, by the regular solution hypothesis explored in Chapter 3, is zero, so we are left with

$$F^E \approx A_V^E = E_V^E - TS_V^E = E_V^E = \Delta E_V^M \tag{7.24}$$

If we now use the solubility parameter equation for ΔE_V^M (Eqn. 7.10), we have for the excess free energy

$$F^E = (x_1 V_1 + x_2 V_2)(\delta_1 - \delta_2)^2 \phi_1 \phi_2 \tag{7.25}$$

or

$$\Delta F^M = RT(x_1 \ln x_1 + x_2 \ln x_2) + (x_1 V_1 + x_2 V_2)(\delta_1 - \delta_2)^2 \phi_1 \phi_2 \tag{7.26}$$

The corresponding molal free energies for the solute are

$$\bar{F}_2^E = RT \ln \gamma_2 = V_2 \phi_1^2 (\delta_2 - \delta_1)^2 \tag{7.27}$$

$$\Delta \bar{F}_2 = RT \ln a_2 = RT \ln x_2 + V_2 \phi_1^2 (\delta_2 - \delta_1)^2 \tag{7.28}$$

It is these equations, arising from a combination of the regular solution concept with assumptions about intermolecular forces (solubility parameter theory) which we shall use in subsequent chapters to interpret the behavior of these solutions. It is important, however, to remember that although Eqns. 7.25 through 7.28 apply to the constant pressure process, the two

[26] A. G. Williamson and R. L. Scott, *J. Phys. Chem.*, **65**, 275 (1961).

terms in Eqns. 7.26 and 7.28, which might be called "configuration" and "interaction" terms respectively, are not separately the entropy and the heat of mixing for the constant pressure process. It also follows that these expressions for the excess free energy cannot be differentiated (with respect to temperature and pressure) to obtain the excess entropy and the excess volume; they are much too approximate for that.

It is for the reader to decide, from the evidence presented in the following chapters and from his own experience, how much reliance to place upon Eqns. 7.25 through 7.28 in estimating and interpreting the properties of solutions. They should never be regarded as a satisfactory substitute for the experimental measurement. They should not be used when there are strong reasons for suspecting the validity of the fundamental assumptions (i.e., random distribution of molecules, geometric mean for the cohesive energy density c_{12}). However, we suggest that these equations, as a "zero[th] approximation," have a wider range of usefulness in dealing with solutions of non-electrolytes than do any other theories. Other theoretical treatments, to be sure, often prove more successful in yielding semiquantitative agreement with the properties of a narrowly restricted group of systems which conform to a special model (e.g., one of the corresponding states theories of solutions applied to mixtures of simple fluids: Ar, Kr, Xe, CH_4, etc.), but they fail badly outside their narrow range of applicability.

In his 1956 review, Scott[27] concluded a discussion of the status of solubility theory of the energy of mixing with these comments:

> Solubility parameter theory does in fact fit the free energy data on most binary systems of non-polar non-electrolytes to within 10 to 20 per cent of thermal energies (60-120 calories per mole 25°C.) or to within the experimental uncertainty of the solubility parameters (which is sometimes large); for heats and excess entropies of mixing, it is somewhat less successful. Considering its almost complete lack of a precise model, it could hardly be expected to give much better agreement; all kinds of minor perturbations can give rise to contributions of magnitudes of small fractions of RT. On the other hand, it follows that when solubility parameters appear to give correct predictions of small values of F^E, etc., the agreement is probably merely fortuitous.

> In short, the solubility parameter equations offer a useful initial approach to a very wide area of solutions, like a small-scale map for a very broad long-distance air view of a subcontinent. It is able to make numerical predictions about all areas; these are unlikely to prove highly accurate when a small area is examined carefully, but they are equally unlikely to prove completely absurd. A really serious failure of solubility parameter theory implies qualitative failure of the basic assumptions and attracts serious attention. . . .

[27] R. L. Scott, *Ann. Rev. Phys. Chem.*, **7**, 43 (1956).

CHAPTER 8

Volume Changes
on Mixing

Of the various ther-
modynamic functions for the mixing process, the volume change
Δv^M on mixing at constant pressure (which is the same as the
excess volume v^E) is one of the most interesting, yet certainly
still one of the least understood. Two aspects of the volume change
problem will be considered here: (1) the correction to "constant
volume" of the experimentally measured quantities for the constant pressure process, and (2) the estimation of the magnitude of
the volume change.

THERMODYNAMIC FUNCTIONS FOR MIXING
AT CONSTANT VOLUME

That the simple
theories of solutions apply more straightforwardly to processes
with zero volume change was recognized at an early stage. In 1929

104

Hildebrand[1] defined a regular solution as one "involving no entropy change when a small amount of one of its components is transferred to it from an ideal solution of the same composition, the total volume remaining unchanged." In 1931 Scatchard[2] derived an expression for the heat of mixing (Eqn. 7.8) with the assumption that the change of volume on mixing is zero.

However, the volume change on mixing at constant pressure is rarely zero, yet it is the constant pressure process which we normally measure in the laboratory. To compare the experimental quantities with these predicted by most theories, it becomes necessary to convert the constant pressure numbers to "constant volume" or vice versa. Methods of making these thermodynamic corrections were first outlined by Scatchard,[3] and have been extensively discussed since.[4,5,6,7] There are in fact several different processes[7] for which the total volume remains constant, but the only one of practical interest is one which starts with the two as-yet-unmixed components in volumes V_1 and V_2, each at the same initial pressure, and each of which ends with the mixture in volume $V_m = V_1 + V_2$ and a different final pressure. The necessary compression or expansion may be performed either on the unmixed components or on the solution; if the necessary data are available for the solution, the latter equations are simpler. If we compress (or expand) the solution by the volume change at constant pressure $\Delta v^M = v^E$ so that

$$v_m = x_1 v_1 + x_2 v_2$$

we obtain for the "constant volume" functions[8] A_V^E, S_V^E, and E_V^E.

$$A_V^E(T,V) - F^E(T,P) = -\frac{1}{2(v\beta)_m}(v^E)^2 + \dots \qquad (8.1)$$

[1] J. H. Hildebrand, *J. Am. Chem. Soc.*, **51**, 66 (1929).

[2] G. Scatchard, *Chem. Revs.*, **8**, 321 (1931).

[3] G. Scatchard, *Trans. Faraday Soc.*, **33**, 160 (1937).

[4] J. H. Hildebrand and R. L. Scott, *Solubility of Nonelectrolytes*, 3rd ed. (Reinhold Publishing Corporation, New York, 1950), pp. 136–143. R. L. Scott, *Discussions, Faraday Soc.*, **15**, 44 (1953).

[5] J. H. Hildebrand and R. L. Scott, *J. Chem. Phys.*, **20**, 1520 (1952).

[6] L. A. K. Staveley, K. R. Hart and W. I. Tupman, *Discussions, Faraday Soc.*, **15**, 130 (1953); *Trans. Faraday Soc.*, **51**, 323 (1955).

[7] R. L. Scott, *J. Phys. Chem.*, **64**, 1241 (1960).

[8] The subscript V here refers to constant volume process or equivalently to the excess functions defined as the difference of the quantity, e.g., for the real mixture in volume V and the ideal mixture in the same volume V, but, of course, at different pressures. The usual excess functions are referred to constant pressure.

$$s_V^E(T,V) - s^E(T,P) = -\left(\frac{\alpha}{\beta}\right)_m (v^E)$$

$$+ \frac{1}{2v\beta}\left(\frac{\partial \ln \beta}{\partial T} + \frac{\alpha}{\beta}\frac{\partial \ln \beta}{\partial P}\right)(v^E)^2 + \dots \quad (8.2)$$

$$E_V^E(T,V) - H^E(T,P) = -T\left(\frac{\alpha}{\beta}\right)_m v^E$$

$$+ \frac{1}{2v\beta}\left(\frac{\partial \ln \beta}{\partial \ln T} + \frac{\alpha T}{\beta}\frac{\partial \ln \beta}{\partial P} + 1\right)(v^E)^2 + \dots \quad (8.3)$$

where α and β are the coefficients of thermal expansion and compressibility, respectively.

Except when the volume changes are large (e.g., greater than 1 cm³ mole⁻¹), the terms in $(v^E)^2$ can be neglected, A_V^E can be set equal to F^E, etc. Table 8.1 illustrates the corrections for the system [7,9,10] n-C_6H_{14} + n-C_6F_{14} for which the volume change is very large.

Table 8.1. SYSTEM n-C_6H_{14} + n-C_6F_{14}, $x = 1/2$, 25°C., $v^E = 4.84$ cm³

	Constant Pressure	Constant Volume	
		Expand unmixed	Compress mixture
F^E, A_V^E/cal	323	316	329
Ts^E, Ts_V^E/cal	193	−23	−48
H^E, E_V^E/cal	516	293	281

It will be noted that this system conforms reasonably well to the regular solution concept, the excess entropy for the constant volume process being small, only 20% of that for the constant pressure process, and that to a good first approximation F^E for the constant pressure process equals E_V^E for the constant volume process. Some of the other systems[6,7] for which the necessary data are available (there are not very many) seem not to support this conclusion, but one must exclude systems with negative excess entropies due to hydrogen bonding (acetone + chloroform). Moreover, systems for which all the excess functions are small (less than about 50 calories) are to the zero*th* approximation ideal and are not suited for testing the validity of a rough concept like that of the "regular solution."

MAGNITUDE OF THE VOLUME CHANGE AT CONSTANT PRESSURE

We turn now to the problem of estimating the volume change on mixing at constant pressure. The notion

[9] R. D. Dunlap, R. G. Bedford, J. G. Woodbury, and S. D. Furrow, *J. Am. Chem. Soc.*, **81**, 2927 (1959).

[10] A. G. Williamson and R. L. Scott, *J. Phys. Chem.*, **65**, 275 (1961).

that positive volume changes (expansions on mixing) are associated with positive deviations from ideality (positive values of F^E) and with the absorption of heat (positive ΔH's), and that negative Δv's are associated with negative deviations or liberation of heat is an old one. Early in his research on solutions, Hildebrand[11] noted an empirical relation between the partial molal Δv and log γ. Figure 8.1 illustrates the relation with the

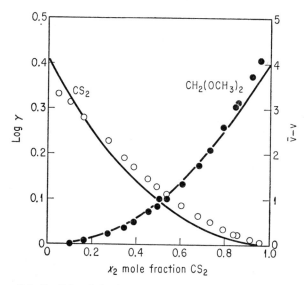

Figure 8.1   Partial molal volumes and activity coefficients in carbon disulfide + methylal solutions.

data of Zawidski[12] and Hubbard[13] for solutions of carbon disulfide and methylal. We see that a reasonable fit is obtained for the relation

$$\log \gamma = (0.10 \text{ cm}^{-3})\Delta \bar{v}.$$

The first attempt to deduce a quantitative relation between volume change and excess free energy was made by Scatchard[3] in 1937. In essence, his derivation proceeded as follows.

We start with the exact thermodynamic relation between excess volume

[11] J. H. Hildebrand, *Solubility*, Reinhold Publishing Corp., 1st ed. (1924), pp. 61–65. See also J. H. Hildebrand and E. D. Eastman, *J. Am. Chem. Soc.*, **37**, 2452 (1915).
[12] J. V. Zawidski, *Z. physik. Chem.*, **35**, 129 (1900).
[13] J. C. Hubbard, *Phys. Rev.*, **30**, 740 (1910); *Z. physik. Chem.*, **74**, 207 (1910).

and the pressure derivative of the excess (Gibbs) free energy and then substitute A^E for F^E:

$$v^E = \left(\frac{\partial F^E}{\partial P}\right)_T = \left(\frac{\partial A_V^E}{\partial P}\right)_T = \left(\frac{\partial E_V^E}{\partial P}\right)_T - T\left(\frac{\partial S_V^E}{\partial P}\right)_T \qquad (8.4)$$

Except for the neglect of the term in $(v^E)^2$ in Eqn. 8.1, Eqn. 8.4 is correct. We now introduce the first important assumption: (1) that in a regular solution, the entropy of mixing is essentially ideal, $s_V^E \approx 0$, and thus is independent of pressure. We can then write

$$v^E = \left(\frac{\partial E_V^E}{\partial P_u}\right)_T = \left(\frac{\partial E_V^E}{\partial v_u}\right)_T\left(\frac{\partial v_u}{\partial P_u}\right)_T = -(\beta v)_u\left(\frac{\partial E_V^E}{\partial V_u}\right)_T \qquad (8.5)$$

Here the subscript u's refer to the pressure, volume, compressibility, etc., of the unmixed initial state of the system ($v_u = x_1 v_1 + x_2 v_2$, etc.) and emphasize the fact that we are no longer dealing with constant pressure processes. We now write $E_V^E = E_m - E_u$, where E_m is the energy of the resultant mixture (at volume v_u); we further replace $(\partial E/\partial v)$ by $n(-E/v)$, where n (Chapter 6, Eqn. 6.17 and Table 6.1) is the ratio of the internal pressure to the cohesive energy density:

$$v^E = -(\beta v)_u\left[\left(\frac{\partial E_m}{\partial v_u}\right)_T - \left(\frac{\partial E_u}{\partial v_u}\right)_T\right] = (\beta v)_u\frac{(n_m E_m - n_u E_u)}{v_u} \qquad (8.6)$$

We now assume (2) that n_m and n_u are essentially the same for the mixture and for the unmixed components, and finally, we (3) invoke again the condition that $s_V^E = 0$ and $E_V^E = F^E$, obtaining

$$v^E = n\frac{(\beta v)_u(E_m - E_u)}{v_u} = n\beta\Delta E_V^M = n\beta F^E \qquad (8.7)$$

For many normal liquids $n \approx 1$, and in the original equation the parameter n was omitted (assumption 4). Equation 8.7 has since been derived in other ways, notably by Longuet-Higgins[14] from first order "conformal solution theory" (a corresponding states approach), in the alternative form

$$\frac{v^E}{v} = \alpha T\frac{F^E}{(-E)} \qquad (8.8)$$

where α is the coefficient of thermal expansion $(\partial \ln v/\partial T)_P$. This equation is, of course, identical to Eqn. 8.7, since at $P \approx 0$,

$$\left(\frac{\partial E}{\partial V}\right)_T \approx T\left(\frac{\partial P}{\partial T}\right)_V = T\frac{\alpha}{\beta} = n\left(\frac{-E}{v}\right)$$

Since $-E/v = \delta^2$, the alternative of $\alpha T/\delta^2$ is suggested for $n\beta$ in Eqn. 8.7.

[14] H. C. Longuet-Higgins, *Proc. Roy. Soc.* (London), **A205**, 247 (1951).

Croll and Scott[15] have compared the volume changes on mixing fluorocarbons and hydrocarbons with the predictions of Eqn. 8.7, as shown in Table 8.2.

Table 8.2. FLUOROCARBON + HYDROCARBON SYSTEMS AT $x_2 = 1/2$

System	T deg K	v^E cc	F^E cal	$\alpha T/\delta^2$ (cc cal$^{-1} \times 10^{-3}$) Fluoro-carbon	Hydro-carbon	Avg.	v^E/F^E (cc cal$^{-1} \times 10^{-3}$)
$CF_4 + CH_4$	107	0.88	86	4.8	7.9	6.3	10.0
n-$C_4F_{10} + n$-C_4H_{10}	233	2.67	255	9.8	6.0	7.9	10.5
n-$C_5F_{12} + n$-C_5H_{12}	266	4.63	285	12.4	6.8	9.6	16.2
n-$C_6F_{14} + n$-C_6H_{14}	298	4.84	328	15.4	8.1	11.7	14.8
$C_7F_{16} + n$-C_7H_{16}	323	5.8	313	16.6	8.3	12.5	19.0

The values of v^E/F^E are appreciably larger than the average of $\alpha T/\delta^2$ for all systems, roughly by about 50 per cent. The qualitative aspects of Eqn. 8.7 fit, but the equation is hardly quantitative. For the example of Fig. 8.1, the constant $n\beta$ is, for carbon disulfide + methylal, about 0.18cc^{-1}, while the coefficient which fits the data is 0.10 cc^{-1}. Here the discrepancy between Eqn. 8.7 and the experiment is in the opposite direction from that of Table 8.2.

Systems with significant negative deviations do show volume contractions (e.g., for acetone + chloroform with a weak hydrogen bond, $v^E = -0.19$ cc, $F^E = -133$ cal), but the quantitative agreement can only be described as poor.

PARTIAL MOLAL VOLUMES IN DILUTE SOLUTIONS

Of special interest are the partial molal volumes of solutes in highly dilute solutions. Differentiation of Eqn. 8.7 in the limit $x_2 \to 0$ yields the equation

$$\bar{V}_2^E = \bar{V}_2 - v_2^o = n_1\beta_1 F_2^E = n_1\beta_1 RT \ln \gamma_2 = \frac{\alpha_1 T}{\delta_1^2} F_2^E \qquad (8.9)$$

The partial molal volumes of I_2 and Br_2 in C_7F_{16} have been measured by Glew[16] and Reeves,[17] and because of their large magnitude provide a severe test for Eqn. 8.9 (Table 8.3). For this fluorocarbon solute, $\beta = 2.34$

[15] I. M. Croll and R. L. Scott, *J. Phys. Chem.*, **62**, 954 (1958).
[16] D. N. Glew and J. H. Hildebrand, *J. Phys. Chem.*, **60**, 616 (1956).
[17] L. W. Reeves and J. H. Hildebrand, *J. Phys. Chem.*, **60**, 949 (1956).

Table 8.3. EXCESS VOLUMES OF SOLUTES IN C_7F_{16}

	$\bar{v}_2$	v_2^o	$\bar{v}_2^E$ obs.	$\bar{v}_2^E$ calc. Eqn. 8.9 (cc)
Iodine	100	59	41	60
Bromine	73	51.5	21	24.7

$\times 10^{-4}$ atm and n = 1.49, far from the value of unity so often assumed. The coefficient $n\beta = \alpha T/\delta^2$ is then 13.9 $\times 10^{-3}$ cc/cal.

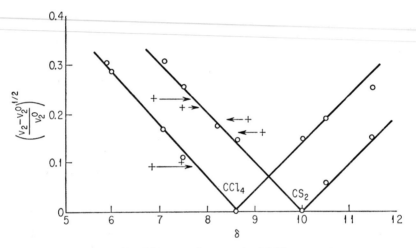

Figure 8.2 Partial excess volumes and solubility parameters.

The agreement is good for bromine, but only fair for iodine; the astonishing feature is that as crude a theory as this can account for this very large partial molal volume at all.

If $\bar{F}_2^E = v_2^o(\delta_1 - \delta_2)^2$, as predicted by solubility parameter theory, this can be substituted into Eqn. 8.9; we obtain

$$\frac{\bar{v}_2 - v_2^o}{v_2^o} = \alpha_1 T \left(\frac{\delta_2 - \delta_1}{\delta_1}\right)^2 \tag{8.10}$$

If this equation is valid, we may expect to be able to plot the excess volumes $\bar{v}_2^E$ for a series of solutes at high dilution in the same solvent as $[(\bar{v}_2 - v_2^o)/v_2^o]^{1/2}$ vs. δ_2 and get straight lines with slope $(\alpha_1 T)^{1/2}/\delta_1$. Fujishiro, Shinoda, and Hildebrand[18] have measured the partial molal

---

[18] R. Fujishiro, K. Shinoda, and J. H. Hildebrand, *J. Phys. Chem.* (December, 1961).

volumes of a large number of solutes at high dilution in CS_2, CCl_4, and n-C_7H_{16}, with the results shown in Table 8.4 and Fig. 8.2.

These partial molal volumes were determined by a dilatometric method, much more expeditious and simple than the usual one of determining densities.

Table 8.4. PARTIAL MOLAL VOLUMES OF SOLUTES AT HIGH DILUTION, 25°C

Solute	δ_2	v_2^o (cc)	$\bar{v}_2$ (cc)		
			in CS_2	in CCl_4	in n-C_7H_{16}
C_7F_{16}	5.85	225.5	...	246.5	254.6
c-$C_6F_{11}CF_3$	6.0	195.8	...	211.6	218.3
i-C_8H_{18}	6.85	166.1	172.2	167.5	167.4
c-$C_4Cl_2F_6$	7.1	142.5	155.5	146.6	153.6
n-C_7H_{16}	7.45	147.5	154.4	149.1	...
$CCl_2F \cdot CClF_2$	7.5	119.8	127.7	120.9	124.5
c-C_6H_{12}	8.2	108.8	112.1	...	...
CCl_4	8.6	97.1	99.2	...	98.2
1,3,5-$(CH_3)_3C_6H_3$	8.8	139.6	144.5	...	...
C_6H_6	9.2	89.3	91.6	...	91.0
C_6H_5Cl	9.5	102.1	...	...	105.5
CS_2	10.0	60.7	...	62.0	63.4
$CHBr_3$	10.5	87.8	88.1	90.9	92.1
Br_2	11.5	51.5	52.6	54.75	...
I_2	14.1	59.0	62.8	66.7	...

We see in Fig. 8.1 that $[(\bar{v}_2 - v_2^o)/v_2^o]^{1/2}$ is, indeed, closely proportional to $\pm(\delta_2 - \delta_1)$, except in the cases of n-C_7H_{16}, i-C_8H_{18}, C_6H_6, and 1,3,5-$(CH_3)_3C_6H_3$ the points for which are designated by crosses. In order to agree with the general pattern, the δ-value of i-C_8H_{18} would have to be 7.7 instead of 6.85. This is practically identical with the values obtained from its solubility relations with C_7F_{16} and I_2, 7.9 and 7.95, respectively. The data for solutes in n-C_7F_{16} are not shown in the figure; they are more scattered, presumably because of the same sort of hydrocarbon irregularities evidenced by the crosses in Fig. 8.2 and discussed further in Chapters 9 and 10.

For both CS_2 and CCl_4 the proportionality constant is close to 0.1 (cc/cal)$^{1/2}$. The square of this, 0.01 cc/cal, does not agree very well with the values of $n\beta = \alpha T/\delta^2$ for the solvents, which are 0.0034 and 0.0049 cc/cal for CS_2 and CCl_4 respectively. While the theory evidently needs re-examination and refinement, it should be realized that the correlation seen in Fig. 8.2, with the coefficient 0.1, extends over an enormous range of expansions up to 9 per cent.

NEGATIVE VOLUME CHANGES

Since 1952, a series of systems have been unearthed for which F^E is positive while v^E is negative, in contradiction with even the qualitative prediction of Eqn. 8.7. Typical of these is the first system examined,[19] carbon tetrachloride $+$ neopentane, for which $v^E = -0.55$ cm^3 and $F^E = 80$ cal at 0°C and $x = \frac{1}{2}$.

Moreover, these results agreed with the prior predictions of Prigogine's[20] "cell theory" and, indeed, with that of any "second order" corresponding states treatment.[21, 22, 23] A detailed discussion of these theories is outside the scope of this book, but it may be useful to outline briefly how these treatments lead to negative volume changes.

In any corresponding states formulation, the thermodynamic properties of a pure substance are expressed as functions of reduced variables. In particular, one can write the volume of a liquid at low (essentially zero) pressure as a function of the temperature, and the two parameters ϵ and σ of the intermolecular pair potential energy:

$$V(T) = N\sigma^3 f\left(\frac{kT}{\epsilon}\right) \tag{8.11}$$

We now consider the special case of mixtures of two different species with the same intrinsic molecular size ($\sigma_{11} = \sigma_{22}$) but differing attractive energies ($\epsilon_{11} \neq \epsilon_{22}$). At any particular temperature, the species with the smaller ϵ (say, ϵ_{22}) will be at the higher reduced temperature kT/ϵ and consequently (since liquids expand with increasing temperature) will have the larger molal volume. We now turn to a mixture of these two liquids, for simplicity at $x = \frac{1}{2}$. The different theories differ somewhat in applying the principle of corresponding states to the mixture, but some appropriate combination of ϵ_{11}, ϵ_{12}, and ϵ_{22} must be used to define a reduced temperature for the mixture; if ϵ_{12} lies between ϵ_{11} and ϵ_{22} (as it will for either an arithmetic mean or geometric mean law), this will be an intermediate reduced temperature. The curve of V against kT/ϵ, is concave upwards (d^2V/dT^2 positive) and against the reciprocal ϵ/kT even more so (Fig. 8.3). Consequently, for any reasonable combining rule, such as

$$\epsilon_m = (\tfrac{1}{2}\epsilon_{11}^{1/2} + \tfrac{1}{2}\epsilon_{22}^{1/2})^2 \qquad\qquad (x = \tfrac{1}{2})$$

[19] V. Mathot and A. Desmyter, *J. Chem. Phys.*, **21**, 782 (1953).

[20] I. Prigogine and V. Mathot, *J. Chem. Phys.*, **20**, 49 (1952). See also I. Prigogine, *The Molecular Theory of Solutions* (North-Holland Publishing Co., Amsterdam, 1957).

[21] I. Prigogine, A. Bellemans and A. Englert-Chwoles, *J. Chem. Phys.*, **24**, 518 (1956).

[22] R. L. Scott, *J. Chem. Phys.*, **25**, 193 (1956).

[23] W. B. Brown, *Phil. Trans. Roy. Soc.* (London), **A250**, 175, 221 (1957).

the volume, v_m, of the mixture will lie close to the mid-point of the curve, below the average volume of the unmixed components, $v_m = \frac{1}{2}(v_1^o + v_2^o)$. The volume change on mixing is thus negative (Fig. 8.3), although the same approach yields a positive excess free energy.

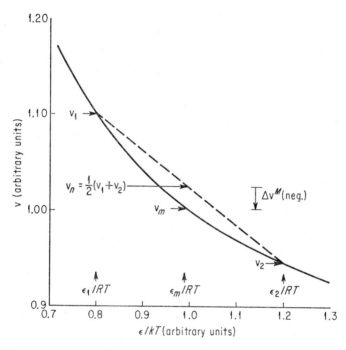

Figure 8.3 Schematic diagram showing how corresponding states theories predict negative volume changes when $\sigma_{11} = \sigma_{22}$ and $\epsilon_{11} \neq \epsilon_{22}$. Scales are arbitrary, but note that origin is not shown. (Slope and curvature from V-T data on CCl_4.)

This exceptional behavior occurs only for mixtures of substances which (1) are sufficiently similar to follow the same law of corresponding states and (2) are very nearly alike in intrinsic size ($\sigma_{11} = \sigma_{22}$); few systems satisfy these conditions. When the σ's are significantly different, corresponding states theories, like Eqn. 8.7, predict positive volume changes with positive excess free energies.

ANALYSIS OF THE VOLUME CHANGE EQUATION

From the foregoing it is abundantly clear that while Eqn. 8.7 is useful for qualitative prediction in many cases, it has very serious shortcomings. As we have seen, the original derivation involved several approximations of uncertain validity. Scott[24] has derived the following more exact equation free from these approximations.

$$v^E = n_m\beta_u F^E \qquad\qquad (0)$$
$$-T(\partial s_V^E/\partial P)_T \qquad\qquad (1)$$
$$+ (n_m\beta_u E_u - x_1 n_1 \beta_1 E_1 - x_2 n_2 \beta_2 E_2) \qquad\qquad (2)$$
$$+ n_m\beta_u T s_V^E \qquad\qquad (3) \quad (8.12)$$

where n_1, n_2, and n_m are the ratios of internal pressure to cohesive energy density for the two pure components and the resulting mixture (at the initial volume) respectively, and

$$\beta_u = \phi_1\beta_1 + \phi_2\beta_2$$

This complicated equation is useless for any *a priori* prediction, but when extensive data [including $(\partial P/\partial T)_V$ measurements on the mixture] are available, one may back-calculate to assess the contributions of the various terms in Eqn. 8.12. The four terms are, of course, (0) the approximate Eqn. 8.7; (1) that which was ignored when we approximated $\partial s_V^E/\partial P = 0$; (2) that which was ignored by the second approximation, that n was the same for the mixture and for the two components; (3) that due to the failure of the third approximation, that $s_V^E = 0$ (the regular solution assumption).

Table 8.5 illustrates the decomposition of Eqn. 8.12 for four systems. After seeing how large some of the neglected terms are, one cannot help being surprised that Eqn. 8.7 has been at all useful. Several features are worth mentioning: (a) The regular solution assumption ($s_V^E = 0$) is reasonably valid in the sense that term (3) is small, but $(\partial s_V^E/\partial P)$ can be quite large. (b) The two correction terms (1) and (2) are usually of opposite sign and to a large extent cancel.

We suspect that any agreement between Eqn. 8.7 and experimental data is, for small volume changes, fortuitous, but for large volume changes the approximate cancellation of (1) and (2) is such as to leave term (0) (Eqn. 8.7) the dominant factor in determining the magnitude of the volume. However, much more work, both theoretical and experimental, will be

[24] R. L. Scott, Meeting of the National Academy of Sciences, November, 1955. To be published.

needed before we can feel any confidence in dealing with problems of volume change.

Table 8.5. BREAKDOWN ANALYSIS OF THE VOLUME CHANGE IN FOUR SYSTEMS

System	t deg C	Terms in v^E (cc)				
		(0)	(1)	(2)	(3)	obs.
$CCl_4 + SiCl_4$	25	0.18	−1.35	1.17	0.01	0.01
$C_6H_6 + C_2H_4Cl_2$	25	0.03	0.18	0.09	−0.06	0.24
$CCl_4 + C(CH_3)_4$	0	0.63	4.5	−6.0	0.27	−0.52
$n\text{-}C_6F_{14} + n\text{-}C_6H_{14}$	25	3.9	−6.4	6.7	0.2	4.84

CHAPTER 9

Regular Solutions
of Solids

IODINE

Extensive data are now available for solutions of I_2, SnI_4 and S_8. Figure 9.1 is a plot of $\log x_2$ vs. $\log T$ for many solutions of I_2. Those which can be classed as violet are represented by solid lines, the non-violet by broken lines.

The line for the activity of solid iodine has been calculated from the heat of fusion and Δc_p by Eqn. 2.43, using $\Delta H^F = 3740$ cal, $c_p^l = 19.5$, $c_p^s = 13.07 + 3.21 \cdot 10^{-4}(t - 25°)^2$ cal/deg as determined by Frederick and Hildebrand,[1] and $T_m = 386.75°K$. These figures give $a_2^s = 0.258$ at 25 deg. This value is somewhat uncertain in view of the long extrapolation of c_p^l to 25 deg from the melting point at 113.6 deg. It should be regarded as a parameter moderately adjustable for the sake of over-all consistency. The same is true of the solubility parameter of iodine, as obtained by the likewise

[1] K. J. Frederick and J. H. Hildebrand, *J. Am. Chem. Soc.*, **60**, 1436 (1938).

116

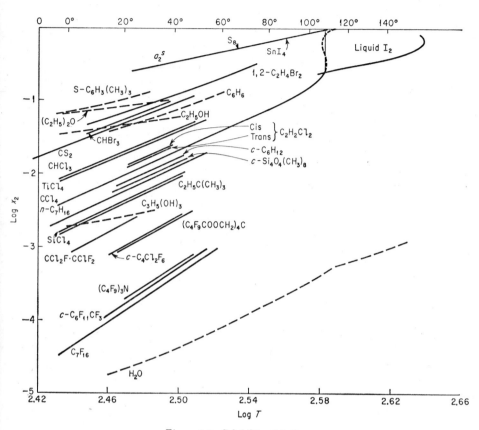

Figure 9.1   Solubility of iodine.

extrapolated value of the heat of vaporization of liquid iodine at 25 deg.

Because of the large role played by iodine solutions in the evolution of regular solution theory, the pertinent solubility data for iodine are summarized, with references, in Appendix 4.

Several features of Fig. 9.1 are noteworthy.

1. *The lines for all violet solutions in the region where $x_2 < 0.1$ are quite straight.* This linearity provides a criterion for accuracy of measurement and also permits accurate determination of entropy and prediction of the variation of solubility with temperature.

2. The equation of the line for CCl_4 solutions is S-shaped in the region approaching the melting point of iodine and is cut by the loop for the

equilibrium between two liquid phases. This portion of the system will be discussed in Chapter 10.

3. The solubilities of iodine in *cis*- and *trans*-dichloroethylenes[2] differ by less than 2 per cent, despite the fact that the dipole moment of the *cis*-form is 1.90 debye units and that of the *trans*-form is zero.

The fact that *it is the individual polar groups that affect solubility relations, not the total dipole moment of the molecule,* is well illustrated also by solutions of the three dinitrobenzenes in benzene. The excess of their partial molal free energies in benzene solution over the ideal partial molal free energies at the same mole fraction are plotted against the square of the mole fraction of benzene. The data used are heats of fusion by Andrews, Lynn, and Johnston[3] and freezing point data by Dahms.[4]

These systems obey the relation $\bar{F}_2 - \bar{F}_2^i = Bx_1^2$ closely enough to permit plotting them together, as shown in Fig. 9.2, which shows also data

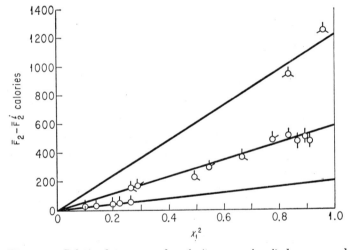

Figure 9.2 Relation between number of nitrogroups in nitrobenzenes and deviation from Raoult's law in benzene solutions.

for the mono- and tri-substituted compounds. The ticks indicate the number and positions of the nitro-groups. It is evident that it is the number, not the position, of the nitro-groups that mainly determines the departure from Raoult's law.

4. *The lines for non-violet solutions have smaller slopes,* corresponding to smaller entropy of solution, the result of complexing, which reduces the

[2] H. A. Benesi and J. H. Hildebrand, *J. Am. Chem. Soc.*, **70**, 3978 (1948).

[3] D. H. Andrews, G. Lynn, and J. Johnston, *J. Am. Chem. Soc.*, **48**, 1274 (1926).

[4] A. Dahms, *Wied. Ann.*, **54**, 496 (1895).

number of independent molecules. These lines curve upward as the complexing decreases with rising temperature.

The degree of complexing must be determined from the departure of the solubility from what it would be if the solution were regular, not from its departure from the value for an ideal solution. Benzene, for example, has a solubility parameter close to that of chloroform, and hence the degree of complexing of iodine dissolved in it is to be obtained from the distance of its line above a position close to the chloroform line, *not* from its distance below the ideal line. Benesi and Hildebrand[5] found this enhancement of solubility to agree satisfactorily with the degree of complexing as determined spectroscopically, both in benzene and in mesitylene.

A sensitive test for complexing is shown in Fig. 9.3, where $R(\partial \ln x_2/\partial \ln T)_{sat}$ is plotted against $-R \ln x_2$. The "Henry's law" factor, $\partial \ln a_2/\partial \ln x_2$, of Eqn. 3.5, used in Figs. 3.3 and 3.5, to convert the ordinate to entropy, is here omitted in order to use none but experimental quantities.

This plot reveals the following significant facts:

1. Complexing increases strongly in the following order: benzene, *p*-xylene, mesitylene, in agreement with the spectroscopic evidence given in Chapter 6.

2. Complexing is very strong in ether, alcohol, glycerin, and water.

One of the evidences of complexing is a smaller partial molal volume than would otherwise be the case. This is illustrated by the values in Table 9.1, obtained by Shinoda and Hildebrand.[6]

Table 9.1. PARTIAL MOLAL VOLUMES OF I_2 AT 25° IN COMPLEXING AND NON-COMPLEXING SOLVENTS, cc/mole

Non-complexing		Complexing	
$c\text{-}Si_4O_4(CH_3)_8$	66.6	$(C_2H_5O)_4Si$	60.5
$SiCl_4$	67.1	C_6H_6	62.4
$c\text{-}C_6H_{12}$	68.2	$C_6H_5CH_3$	61.6
CCl_4	66.7	$p\text{-}C_6H_4(CH_3)_2$	62.5
$CHCl_3$	65.6	$1,3,5\text{-}(CH_3)_3C_6H_3$	62.7
CS_2	60.7	$1,4\text{-}C_{10}H_7(CH_3)_2$	52.2
		$n\text{-}(C_4H_9)_2O$	56.0

3. The solutions in bromoform, the two dichloroethanes and the two dichloroethylenes, which might pass for non-solvated solutions on the evi-

[5] H. A. Benesi and J. H. Hildebrand, *J. Am. Chem. Soc.*, **71**, 2703 (1949).

[6] K. Shinoda and J. H. Hildebrand, *J. Phys. Chem.*, **62**, 295 (1958). See also W. B. Jepson and J. S. Rowlinson, *J. Chem. Soc.*, **261**, 1278 (1956).

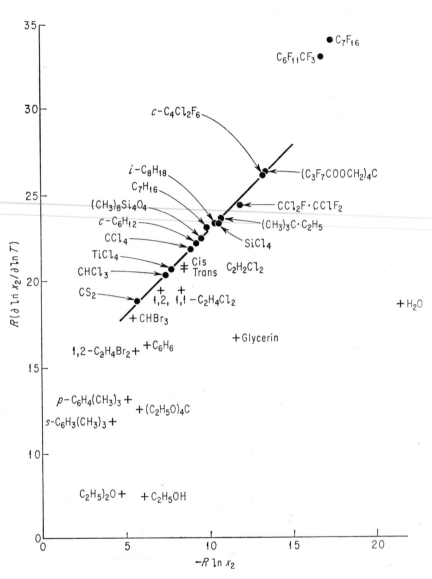

Figure 9.3 Effect of complexing upon entropy of solution of iodine. Non-violet solutions denoted by +.

dence of Fig. 9.1, are seen in Fig. 9.3 to be slightly solvated. This prompted a re-examination of the adsorption spectra of these solutions by Walkley, Glew, and Hildebrand,[7] referred to in Chapter 6. A plot of their preliminary results, not included in their paper, is here shown in Fig. 9.4. Instead of

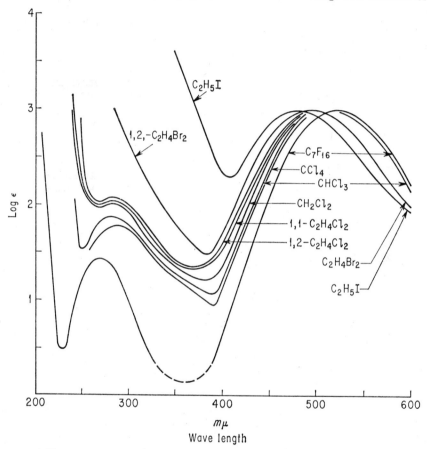

Figure 9.4 Extinction coefficients of iodine solution normalized to equal values for the visible band.

rigidly controlling concentrations, the peak heights were normalized to the value for the solution in f-heptane. Although several of these solutions were originally classed as violet, the gradual shift from violet in C_7H_{16} and CCl_4 to a distinct brown in C_2H_5I is quite evident. There is obviously a gradual transition from the non-specific, physical, London force type of interaction to a specific, chemical, donor-acceptor interaction.

[7] J. Walkley, D. N. Glew, and J. H. Hildebrand, *J. Chem. Phys.*, **33**, 621 (1960).

4. The contrast between two silicones is most interesting. The molecules of octamethyl-tetrasiloxane, c-$(CH_3)_8 Si_4O_4$, contain an octagonal core of alternating silicon and oxygen atoms, with two methyl groups attached to each atom of silicon. A scale model indicates that the methyl groups are most evenly distributed when the silicon atoms are about halfway between a tetrahedral and a square configuration. The methyl groups then so shield the oxygen atoms that they cannot act as donors to iodine molecules; consequently, the solution is quite violet in color and its point falls on the line with other violet solutions in Fig. 9.3. It behaves toward iodine like a compact, paraffin molecule. The tetra-ethoxysilane, on the other hand, strongly complexes with iodine. The point for its solution is far below the line for uncomplexed solutions, and its color is brown.

CORRELATION OF SOLUBILITY OF IODINE WITH SOLUBILITY PARAMETERS

The degree of agreement between measured solubilities and the predictions of regular solution theory in its simplest form can be seen in Table 9.2, where values of the solubility parameter of iodine are shown, calculated from the measured values x_2 in each solution, with v_2^o taken as 59 cc and $a_2^s = 0.258$. We combine Eqns. 2.33b and 7.28 to obtain

$$\ln a_2^s = \ln x_2 + \frac{v_2\phi_1^2(\delta_2 - \delta_1)^2}{RT} \tag{9.1}$$

The solvents are arranged in groups in order to bring out the differences in the strength of interaction between molecules of different types mentioned in Chapter 6. One sees that (1) CS_2 and the three tetrahalides give virtually identical values for the solubility parameter of iodine, 14.1, despite values of $100x_2$ ranging from 5.58 to 0.499. (2) The δ-values of the fluorocarbons and the chlorofluorocarbons thus calculated are all slightly higher than those of the first group. (3) The values calculated for the two paraffins, i-C_8H_{18} and $(CH_3)_3CC_2H_5$, are 1 unit smaller. The discrepancy is less for n-C_7H_{16} and practically vanishes for c-C_6H_{12}. Comparable discrepancies are found in all mixtures containing these paraffins.

The problem presented by these three groups of solvents is not confined to the regular solution treatment; it may render inaccurate any formulation of potential between molecules of unlike species which neglects differences between types of structure such as those which exist in (1) aliphatic hydrocarbons, with none but bonding electrons, and (2) others which have outer, non-bonding electrons.

Table 9.2. SOLUBILITY PARAMETER OF IODINE FROM
SOLUBILITY IN DIFFERENT TYPES OF SOLVENTS

	δ_1	δ_2
CS_2	10.0	14.1
$TiCl_4$	9.0	14.1
CCl_4	8.6	14.2
$SiCl_4$	7.6	14.1
$CCl_2F \cdot CClF_2$	7.5	14.3
$2,2,3\text{-}C_4Cl_3F_7$	6.9	14.3
$c\text{-}C_4Cl_2F_6$	7.1	14.4
$(C_4F_9)_3N$	5.9	14.4
$c\text{-}C_6F_{11}CF_3$	6.2	14.6
C_7F_{16}	5.9	14.4
$CHCl_3$	9.3	14.3
$CHBr_3$	10.5	14.5
$c\text{-}C_6H_{12}$	8.2	14.0
$n\text{-}C_7H_{16}$	7.5	13.5
$i\text{-}C_8H_{18}$	6.9	13.1
$(CH_3)_3C \cdot C_2H_5$	6.7	13.1
$c\text{-}(CH_3)_8Si_4O_4$	(6.4) see text	(12.3)

The case of octamethyl-tetrasiloxane is interesting, since it presents an extreme case of a non-central intermolecular potential. The value 6.4 for its solubility parameter is obtained from its energy of vaporization divided by its molal volume, 312 cc. However, considerable part of this volume is contributed by the Si_4O_4 core, whereas its intermolecular attractive field resides almost entirely in the eight peripheral methyl groups. Experimentally, it lies between cyclohexane and normal heptane in solvent power. This is a case that invites treatment in terms of a Kihara potential; as a practical measure, however, it can be handled, like the pure aliphatic solvents, by an empirical correction to its solubility parameter, as described in Chapter 10.

Chloroform and bromoform are listed separately, because they are the only solvents in the table with permanent dipoles. These dipoles are apparently so shielded as to have little effect.

SOLUBILITY IN A MIXED SOLVENT

Smith, Walkley, and Hildebrand[8] determined the increase in solubility of iodine in C_7F_{16} upon addition of CCl_4 as follows: volume per cent CCl_4 8.93 and 12.50, $100x_2$ 0.0388 and 0.0545, respectively. These figures afford a test of the equation for the solubility parameter of a mixed solvent;

$$\delta_m = \frac{\phi_1\delta_1 + \phi_3\delta_3}{\phi_1 + \phi_3}$$

With $\delta_1 = 5.85$ for C_7F_{16} and $\delta_2 = 14.38$ for I_2 and $\delta_3 = 8.60$ for CCl_4, one obtains the line for log x_2 vs. volume fraction of CCl_4 shown in Fig. 9.5.

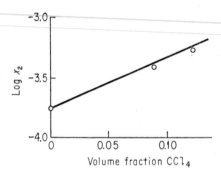

Figure 9.5 Change in solubility of iodine in C_7F_{16} on addition of CCl_4.

The two measured values are in excellent agreement with the theoretical line.

When the solubility parameter of the solid solute lies between those of two solvents, the solubility will be greater in certain mixtures than in either pure liquid, and, if solubility parameter theory is completely valid, should equal the ideal solubility when the solvent ratio ϕ_1/ϕ_3 yields $\delta_m = \delta_2$. Gordon and Scott[9] measured the solubility of phenanthrene ($\delta_2 = 9.8$) in mixtures of cyclohexane ($\delta_1 = 8.2$) and methylene iodide ($\delta_3 = 11.8$), and found the expected enhancement of solubility, but the solubility in the best solvent mixture fell short of the ideal. Apparently, this lack of agreement is due to the (quantitative) failure of solubility parameter equations to fit the binary interaction between phenanthrene and cyclohexane, $A_{12} > (\delta_1 - \delta_2)^2$.

STANNIC IODIDE

The solubility relations of stannic iodide closely parallel those of iodine and sulfur, as indicated in Fig. 9.6. Its molecule is a regular tetrahedron; its bonds are highly covalent, as indicated by its orange color.[10] It differs from iodine in being a potential electron-donor rather than an acceptor. Its molal heat of fusion, its heat capacity of solid and liquid, and its vapor pressure were determined by

[8] E. B. Smith, J. Walkley, and J. H. Hildebrand, *J. Phys. Chem.*, **63**, 703 (1959).

[9] L. J. Gordon and R. L. Scott, *J. Am. Chem. Soc.*, **74**, 4138 (1952).

[10] K. S. Pitzer and J. H. Hildebrand, *J. Am. Chem. Soc.*, **63**, 2472 (1941).

Negishi.[11] Its melting point is 144.5 deg; its molal heat of fusion was determined as 4600 cal at the melting point, and $\Delta c_p = 5.7$ cal/deg. These figures give the molal entropy of fusion as 9.1 cal/deg at 25 deg, and the activity of the solid as 0.113 at the same temperature. This value for the entropy of fusion is in excellent agreement with the intercept of the entropy of solution of iodine at $R \ln x_2 = 0$ in Fig. 3.6.

In order to obtain a figure for the solubility parameter, we use an expression given by Kelley[12] for the heat of vaporization, $\Delta h^V = (25{,}000 - 18\ T)$ cal. This, with the molal volume of the liquid extrapolated from densities measured by Negishi, 151 cc, gives $\delta_2 = 11.2$. This figure involves such long extrapolations that it is inferior, for practical purposes, to a mean value obtained from solubility data.

Dorfman and Hildebrand[13] determined the solubility of SnI_4 between 10 deg and 40 deg in n-heptane, ether, carbon tetrachloride, chloroform, benzene, toluene, m-xylene, ethylene bromide, and carbon disulfide, and in sulfur at 104 deg and 130 deg. Reinders and deLange[14] and also van Klooster have determined melting points for the system $SnI_4 + I_2$. Hildebrand and Negishi[15] determined the solubility in $SiCl_4$. Smith and Walkley[16] determined it in

$$CHBr_3, \quad CCl_4, \quad CCl_2F \cdot CClF_2, \quad c\text{-}C_4Cl_2F_6, \quad c\text{-}C_6F_{11}CF_3, \quad \text{and} \quad C_7F_{16}$$

McLaughlin and Scott[17] determined it in $(C_4F_9)_3N$ and in the cyclic ether of uncertain structure, $C_8F_{16}O$.

Nearly all of the available data covering a range of temperature are plotted in Fig. 9.6 as $\log x_2$ vs. $\log T$. The plot closely resembles the one for iodine solutions, except for the absence of cases of marked solvation. The absorption spectrum of SnI_4 in its solutions in $CHCl_3$, CCl_4, $n\text{-}C_7H_{16}$ and $c\text{-}C_4Cl_2F_6$ all show a strong band with a maximum at 359–361 mμ and a weaker one at 283–286 mμ. In benzene, the former is unchanged, but the latter is shifted to 296 mμ and strongly enhanced.

These solutions are like iodine solutions also in offering the clear evidence seen in Fig. 3.5, of virtually ideal entropy of solution at constant volume.

As in the case of iodine solutions, values for the solubility parameter of SnI_4 have been calculated from solubility, with results shown in Table 9.2. We see here also that the aliphatic hydrocarbons give δ-values for

[11] G. R. Negishi, *J. Am. Chem. Soc.*, **58**, 2293 (1936).

[12] K. K. Kelley, *Bull. U.S. Bur. Mines*, **383** (1934).

[13] M. E. Dorfman and J. H. Hildebrand, *J. Am. Chem. Soc.*, **49**, 729 (1929).

[14] W. Reinders and S. deLange, *Z. anorg. Chem.*, **79**, 230 (1912).

[15] J. H. Hildebrand and G. R. Negishi, *J. Am. Chem. Soc.*, **59**, 330 (1937).

[16] E. B. Smith and J. Walkley, *Trans. Faraday Soc.*, **56**, 220 (1960).

[17] E. P. McLaughlin and R. L. Scott, *J. Am. Chem. Soc.*, **76**, 5276 (1954).

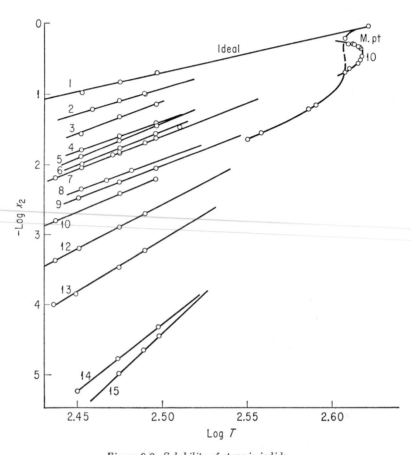

Figure 9.6 Solubility of stannic iodide.

1. CS$_2$	9. n-C$_7$H$_{16}$
2. CHBr$_3$	10. SiCl$_4$
3. 1,2-C$_2$H$_4$Br$_2$	11. i-C$_3$H$_{18}$
4. C$_6$H$_5$CH$_3$	12. CCl$_2$F·CClF$_2$
5. C$_6$H$_6$	13. c-C$_4$Cl$_2$F$_6$
6. CHCl$_3$	14. c-C$_6$F$_1$CF$_3$
7. CCl$_4$	15. C$_7$F$_{16}$
8. (C$_2$H$_5$)$_2$O	

SnI$_4$ about 1 unit lower, and that the fluorocarbons give values a little higher than do the two tetrahalides.

The solubility in CS$_2$, 14.64 mole per cent, is appreciably higher than the value we have calculated from the activity of solid SnI$_4$, 11.3 per cent; whether this is the result of solvation or of the unavoidable uncertainty in the figure for a_2^s is not clear. An acid character of CS_2 is evident in its reaction with alkyl sulfides, and may operate here (see further Chapter 10). Furthermore, solubility increases in the order benzene, toluene, m-xylene, the order of decreasing ionization potential, instead of decreasing in the order of solubility parameters.

Table 9.3. SOLUBILITY PARAMETER OF STANNIC IODIDE FROM SOLUBILITY IN DIFFERENT TYPES OF SOLVENTS

	$100x_2$	δ_1	δ_2
$SiCl_4$	0.382	7.6	11.4
CCl_4	1.459	8.6	11.6
$CCl_2F \cdot CClF_2$	0.128	7.5	11.8
$c\text{-}C_4Cl_2F_6$	0.0342	7.1	11.9
$c\text{-}C_6F_{11}CF_3$	0.00163	6.1	12.1
$(C_4F_9)_3N$	0.00115	5.9	12.0
C_7F_{16}	0.00100	5.9	12.0
C_7H_{16}	0.553	7.5	10.3
$i\text{-}C_8H_{18}$	0.321	6.9	10.7
$(C_2H_5)_2O$	0.690	7.4	10.9
$CHCl_3$	1.692	9.3	11.9
$CHBr_3$	8.02	10.5	12.0
$C_2H_4Br_2$	4.71	10.4	12.6
C_6H_6	2.181	9.2	11.8
$C_6H_5CH_3$	2.507	8.9	11.6
$m\text{-}C_6H_4(CH_3)_2$	2.558	8.8	11.4

SULFUR

The solubility relations of rhombic sulfur,[18] S_8, are similar to those of iodine and stannic iodide, and, for non-polar solvents, are similarly predictable, as shown by the simple correlation plotted in Fig. 3.6.

PHOSPHORUS

Active (white) phosphorus, P_4, is an especially interesting solute. Although its melting point is 44.10 deg, it is subject to enormous supercooling, and its activity and molal

[18] J. H. Hildebrand and C. A. Jenks, *J. Am. Chem. Soc.*, **43**, 2172 (1921).

volume as liquid below the melting point are not subject to the uncertainty of the long extrapolations required in the case of other solids. Its molal heat of fusion is very small, 601 cal, according to Young and Hildebrand,[19] who determined also its heat capacity as both solid and liquid. The activity of the solid is extraordinarily high, 0.865 at 0 deg and 0.941 at 25 deg.

The P_4 molecule is a regular tetrahedron, highly polarizable, and it evidently has a great deal of rotational energy in the solid form. Its molal entropy of fusion is 1.895 cal/deg. Its liquid molal volume is 69.4 cc at 0 deg and 70.4 cc at 25 deg.

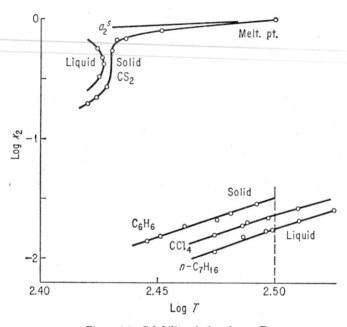

Figure 9.7   Solubility of phosphorus, P_4.

Its solubility in CS_2 was determined by Cohen and Inouye,[20] in C_6H_6 by Christomanos,[21] and in CCl_4 and n-C_7H_{16} by Groot and Hildebrand.[22] The data in these solvents are plotted in Fig. 9.7 together with points for liquid P_4 and CS_2 obtained by Hildebrand and Buehrer.[23]

[19] F. E. Young and J. H. Hildebrand, *J. Am. Chem. Soc.*, **64,** 839 (1942).
[20] E. Cohen and K. Inouye, *Z. physik. Chem.*, **72,** 411 (1910).
[21] A. C. Christomanos, *Zeits. anorg. allgem. Chem.*, **45,** 132 (1905).
[22] C. Groot and J. H. Hildebrand, *J. Am. Chem. Soc.*, **70,** 3815 (1948).
[23] J. H. Hildebrand and T. F. Buehrer, *J. Am. Chem. Soc.*, **42,** 2213 (1920).

The interesting features of this plot are the following:

1. The lines for CCl_4 and C_7H_{16} break at the melting point of P_4 with a change in slope corresponding to the slope of the line for a_2^s above.

2. The solubility parameter of P_4 calculated from its solubility in CCl_4 is 14.5; in C_7H_{16} it is 13.4, the same sort of discrepancy as was found for iodine in aliphatic hydrocarbons, seen in Table 8.2.

3. The peculiar shape of the curve for solid P_4 in CS_2, which puzzled Cohen and Inouye, is in good accord with the solubility equation and the nearly tangent liquid-liquid curve.

NAPHTHALENE

Scatchard[24] compared the measured solubilities of naphthalene at 20 deg with values calculated by the methods herein described. These figures are reproduced in Table 9.4 (his values of $\Delta E^V/v$).

Table 9.4. SOLUBILITY OF NAPHTHALENE AT 20°

Solvent	$\Delta E^V/v$ calories per cc	v cc	Solubility, x_2 Measured	Calculated
Naphthalene (ideal)	101.5	123.00	0.261	0.261
Chlorobenzene	93.4	101.63	0.256	0.256
Benzene	83.9	88.89	0.241	0.240
Toluene	81.0	106.31	0.224	0.228
Carbon tetrachloride	76.1	96.45	0.205	0.210
Hexane	54.2	130.47	0.090	0.067
Aniline	154.5	91.06	0.130	0.110
Nitrobenzene	143.1	101.95	0.243	0.158
Acetone	97.0	73.34	0.183	0.260
n-Butyl alcohol	123.7	91.45	0.0495	0.232
Methyl alcohol	213.7	40.44	0.0180	0.00075
Acetic acid	172.6	57.23	0.0456	0.0540

If we examine the solubility of naphthalene in the more polar solvents, which have been segregated from the others at the bottom of Table 9.4,

[24] G. Scatchard, *Chem. Revs.*, **8**, 329 (1931).

we may observe significant differences. It is evident that dipole moment alone cannot account for the departure from ideal behavior. Of the three similar molecules, chlorobenzene, nitrobenzene and aniline, the one possessing the largest dipole moment, nitrobenzene, is not the one showing the largest diminution in solvent power for the non-polar solute, naphtha-

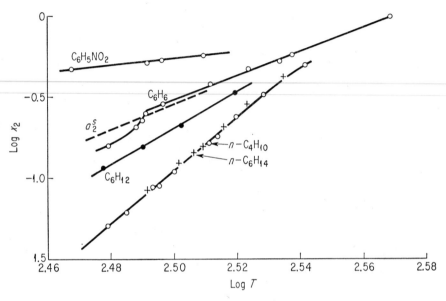

Figure 9.8 Solubility of Al_2Br_6.

lene; on the contrary, this solvent, together with chloroform and chloro-benzene, are nearly ideal solvents for naphthalene, while aniline, with a dipole moment of only 1.51, is the poorest. This affords evidence for the role of the hydrogen bond as a factor in intermolecular action. Phenol, like aniline, is a comparatively poor solvent. No figure for it has been included in the table, because the eutectic point of this solution lies above 25 deg; however, a plot of the data[25] shows that its solvent power for naphthalene is less than that of aniline. Ethyl alcohol, in which the hydrogen bond is strong, is a still poorer solvent. Ether and chloroform, in spite of their dipole moments in excess of 1 debye unit, do not lose in solvent power on that account. The relations show that the hydrogen

[25] W. H. Hatcher and F. W. Skirrow, *J. Am. Chem. Soc.*, **39**, 1939 (1917).

bond is a far more important factor than dipole moment in "squeezing out" non-polar molecules.

ALUMINUM BROMIDE

Solutions of Al_2Br_6 illustrate several interesting features. In Figure 9.8 are plotted solubilities in $C_6H_5NO_2$ by Menshutkin,[26] in C_6H_6 by Eley and King,[27] in c-C_6H_{12} by Leighton and Wilkes,[28] in n-C_6H_{12} by Boedeker and Oblad,[29] and in n-C_4H_{10} by Heldman and Thurmond.[30] Its melting point is 97.5 deg. We select $\Delta_H{}^F = 5.4$ kcal from several somewhat divergent values and calculate $a_2^s = 0.168$ at 25 deg.

The most interesting feature is the near coincidence of the points for the benzene solution with the ideal line, despite the considerable difference in solubility parameters. Eley and King[31] have given $\delta = 11.9$ for Al_2Br_6; for benzene, $\delta = 9.15$. This is obviously a pseudo-ideal solution; Eley and King found a strong absorption band at 2785 Å, and a compound freezes out non-congruently, as seen in the curve.

The coincidence between the points for butane and hexane is explained by the fact that in this temperature range the former is under considerable pressure.

In nitrobenzene, the dimer is evidently dissociated into monomers, and probably is solvated.

Kavelev and Monroe[32] have reported figures for the solubility of Al_2Br_6 in CS_2. Their points fall close to the ideal. They report a strong darkening of color, a fact which indicates that CS_2 *can* act as an electron donor. This, together with the acceptor capacity suggested by its reaction with alkyl sulfides, and possibly with SnI_4, C_6H_6 and $C_6H_5CH_3$, mentioned earlier, indicates that mixtures with CS_2 may not always be purely physical in character.

SOLUBILITY AND MELTING POINT

The effect of difference in melting points upon the solubility of otherwise similar solutes should not be overlooked. The three dinitrobenzenes whose excess free energies are

[26] B. N. Menshutkin, Seidel-Linke, *Solubilities of Inorganic and Metal Organic Compounds* (D. Van Nostrand Co., Inc., New York, 1958).

[27] D. D. Eley and D. J. King, *Trans. Faraday Soc.*, **47**, 1287 (1951).

[28] P. A. Leighton and J. B. Wilkes, *J. Am. Chem. Soc.*, **70**, 2600 (1948).

[29] E. R. Boedeker and A. G. Oblad, ibid., **69**, 2036 (1947).

[30] J. D. Heldman and C. D. Thurmond, ibid., **66**, 427 (1944).

[31] D. D. Eley and P. J. King, *J. Chem. Soc.*, **1952**, 4972.

[32] H. H. Kavelev and C. J. Monroe, ibid., **50**, 2421 (1928).

represented in Fig. 9.2 have very different solubilities in benzene, as shown in Table 9.5, because a_2^s decreases with temperature below the melting point (cf. Chapter 2); although at equal mole fractions in solution their activities are virtually the same.

Table **9.5.** INFLUENCE OF THE MELTING POINTS OF THE THREE DINITROBENZENES UPON THEIR SOLUBILITY IN BENZENE

	t_m °C	Solubility, mole per cent at 50°
Meta	90	37.6
Ortho	116	17.5
Para	170	3.1

CHAPTER 10

Liquid-Liquid Mixtures

MEASURES OF ACTIVITY

The two commonly used measures of the activities of the components of liquid mixtures are (1) vapor pressures, for completely miscible liquids, and (2) mutual solubility or critical temperature and composition for mixtures of limited solubility. Systems with two liquid phases offer the advantage of presenting larger deviations from ideality, and put greater strains upon any theory, but we first consider vapor pressures.

VAPOR PRESSURES

Total vapor pressure is easily measured, but it is considered desirable to know the partial pressures, and it is usually difficult to measure vapor compositions accurately, especially in the region where one component is dilute. Moreover, unless the pressures are low, accurate corrections for derivations from ideal gas behavior must be made. Furthermore, vapor pressures are most conveniently measured in a region of temperature appropriate for a particular mixture, and it is sometimes difficult to reduce results on different systems to a common temperature in order to make systematic comparisons such as are possible with the solubility of gases and of solids.

If the total vapor pressure is measured over the whole composition range, one may calculate the partial pressures with the aid of the Gibbs-Duhem equation. Barker[1] has outlined successive approximation methods for deducing excess free energies from total pressure data, and Myers and Scott[2] have refined his procedures for data processing with high speed electronic computers.

Williamson and Scott[3] have recently found that the data on the system $C_6F_{14} + C_6H_{14}$ show more consistency and a better fit if only total vapor pressures are used, and if the extra vapor composition data are disregarded. They urge a careful re-examination of the whole problem of deriving free energies from vapor pressure data to see whether the extra effort required to measure vapor compositions in an equilibrium still is worthwhile.

The simplest measure of the non-ideality of a liquid mixture is the percentage excess of its total vapor pressure over the mole fraction average of the vapor pressure of the pure constituents. There are many **nearly ideal binary mixtures** of closely related substances. Examples are shown in Table 10.1. Their approximate ideality accords with the small differences

Table 10.1. APPROXIMATELY IDEAL LIQUID MIXTURES

Components		$\dfrac{100(P - P^i)}{P}$	$t°$	$\pm(\delta_2 - \delta_1)$ at 25°	Ref.
$n\text{-}C_7H_{16}$	$i\text{-}C_8H_{18}$	−0.05	97.2	0.6	a
$n\text{-}C_7H_{16}$	$c\text{-}C_6H_{11}CH_3$	∼0	97.2	0.4	a
$n\text{-}C_7H_{16}$	$n\text{-}C_8H_{18}$	−0.06	97.2	0.1	a
$n\text{-}C_7H_{16}$	$C_2H_5CH{=}CHC_3H_7$	∼0	97.2	...	a
C_6H_6	$C_6H_5CH_3$	∼0	79.6	0.25	a
C_6H_6	$C_2H_4Cl_2$	∼0	50.0	0.65	b
C_6H_6	$CHCl_3$	0.8	20.0	0.15	c
CH_3OH	C_2H_5OH	∼0	25.0	...	c
$c\text{-}C_5F_{10}$	$n\text{-}C_5F_{12}$	−0.2	25.0	0.32	d
$c\text{-}C_5F_{10}$	$n\text{-}C_6F_{14}$	1.2	25.0	0.13	d
$(C_4F_9)_3N$	$n\text{-}C_6F_{14}$	0.4	25.0	0.02	d

[a] H. A. Beatty and G. Calingaert, *Ind. Eng. Chem.*, **26**, 504 (1934).
[b] J. von Zawidski, *Z. physik. Chem.*, **35**, 129 (1900).
[c] G. C. Schmidt, ibid., **99**, 71 (1921).
[d] M. M. Newcomb and G. H. Cady, *J. Am. Chem. Soc.*, **78**, 5216 (1956).

[1] J. A. Barker, *Austr. J. Chem.*, **6**, 207 (1953).
[2] D. B. Myers and R. L. Scott, to be published.
[3] A. G. Williamson and R. L. Scott, *J. Phys. Chem.*, **65**, 275 (1961).

in their solubility parameters. The two alcohols, although strongly hydrogen bonding, are so much alike in this and all other respects that they also form a nearly ideal solution. An excellent summary of hydrocarbon mixtures is given by Rowlinson.[4]

Table 10.2. HEATS OF MIXING, AND PER CENT EXCESS TOTAL VAPOR PRESSURES AT $x \approx 0.5$

System	t deg C	$\Delta_H{}^M$ cal	$\Delta_V{}^M$ cm	$\Delta_E{}_V^M$ cal	$\pm(\delta_2 - \delta_1)$ from $\Delta_E{}_V^M$	$\pm(\delta_2 - \delta_1)$ from $(\Delta_E{}^V/\mathrm{v})$	$\dfrac{100(P - P^i)}{P^i}$	at t deg C
$CCl_4 + C_6H_6$	25	26[a,b,f]	0.01	25	0.88	0.55	2.92[d]	40
$CCl_4 + c\text{-}C_6H_{12}$	25	40[a]	0.16	26	1.05	0.40	2.76[d]	40
$C_6H_6 + c\text{-}C_6H_{12}$	25	182[a]	0.65	131	2.31	0.95	12.85	40
$CCl_4 + SiCl_4$	25	32[b]	0.01	31	1.09	1.15	4.55	25
$C_6H_6 + n\text{-}C_7H_{16}$	20	226[e]	0.51	189	2.56	1.70		

[a] J. R. Goates, R. J. Sullivan, and J. B. Ott, *J. Phys. Chem.*, **63**, 589 (1959).

[b] R. D. Vold, *J. Am. Chem. Soc.*, **59**, 1515 (1937).

[c] S. E. Wood, *J. Am. Chem. Soc.*, **59**, 1510 (1937).

[d] G. Scatchard, S. E. Wood, and J. M. Mochel, *J. Am. Chem. Soc.*, **61**, 320 (1939); ibid., **62**, 712 (1940); *J. Phys. Chem.*, **43**, 119 (1939).

[e] C. P. Brown, A. R. Mathieson, and J. C. J. Thynne, *J. Chem. Soc.*, 4141 (1955).

[f] G. H. Cheesman and A. M. B. Whitaker, *Proc. Roy. Soc.* (London), **A212**, 406 (1952).

Systems with heats of mixing and excess total pressures of moderate magnitude are shown in Table 10.2. A great deal of labor has been expended upon the binary mixtures of CCl_4, $c\text{-}C_6H_{12}$, and C_6H_6. The deviations are so small that all the factors involved have had to be measured with painstaking accuracy: gas imperfections, liquid and vapor compositions, volume changes, etc. When all these have been accurately measured, there remain other factors whose effects are difficult to evaluate.

One sees in Table 10.2 that in the case of the system $CCl_4 + SiCl_4$, whose components are of the same electronic type, the difference between the solubility parameters determined from $(\Delta_E{}^V/\mathrm{v})^{1/2}$ agrees excellently with the value calculated from the heat of mixing, but that this is not so in the solutions of the different types: N-electrons, π-electrons, bonding electrons. We saw in Chapter 9 that the solubility parameter of iodine calculated from solutions in chlorides and fluorides has a range of some 0.5, and that between $c\text{-}C_6H_{12}$ and $n\text{-}C_7H_{16}$ it is 0.5. It should be evident, therefore, that simple solubility parameter theory cannot account at all

[4] J. S. Rowlinson, *Liquids and Liquid Mixtures* (Butterworth's Scientific Publications, London, 1959), (Academic Press, Inc., New York, 1959), p. 142 ff.

accurately for excess total pressures of only a few per cent or for heats of mixing of less than 100 cal/mole, especially where the components are of different electron types.

These differences introduce corresponding uncertainty into all current theories. A much more sophisticated analysis of intermolecular forces is needed before systems exhibiting the small deviations illustrated in Table 10.2 can be successfully accounted for.

Various workers have tried to apply corresponding states theories[5],[6] to some of these systems. The first three systems (the triad of C_6H_6, C_6H_{12}, and CCl_4) seem to be described better by the corresponding states approaches, especially by what Scott[6] has called the "two-liquid" model. At best, however, these theories have a very limited range of applicability.

ACID-BASE INTERACTIONS

A factor that may affect deviations of mixtures of CCl_4 and C_6H_6 from any purely physical theory has been brought to light by the rediscovery by Goates, Sullivan, and Ott[7] that a solid 1:1 compound of the two components freezes out at -35 deg. That this is no mere result of crystal packing is indicated by the freezing out of a 1:1 compound of CCl_4 with p-$C_6H_4(CH_3)_2$ at -5 deg. Both are evidently donor-acceptor complexes.

Similar results on the same systems were observed earlier by Kapustinskii and Drakin[8] in the Soviet Union. They deduce by thermal analysis of the cooling curves an exothermic heat of formation for the $CBr_4 + C_6H_6$ complex with $\Delta H = -3.93$ kcal. Goates, et al. estimate for the $CCl_4 + C_6H_6$ complex $\Delta H = -3.5$ kcal. It is surprising that no evidence for such strong compound formation is found in the thermodynamic functions for mixing the two liquids, nor in the calorimetric heats of mixing determined by Goates and his co-workers.

An illuminating example is furnished by solutions of CS_2 with C_6H_6 and with $C_6H_5CH_3$, whose partial and total vapor pressures at 30 deg were measured by Schmidt.[9] Their solubility parameters are 10.0, 9.15, and 8.9, respectively, but $CS_2 + C_6H_5CH_3$, $\delta_1 - \delta_3 = 1.1$, shows an excess total

[5] I. Prigogine, *The Molecular Theory of Solutions* (North-Holland Publishing Company, Amsterdam, 1957). Contains earlier references.

[6] R. L. Scott, *J. Chem. Phys.*, **25**, 193 (1956).

[7] J. R. Goates, R. J. Sullivan, and J. B. Ott, *J. Phys. Chem.*, **63**, 589 (1959).

[8] A. F. Kapustinskii and S. I. Drakin, *Izvestia Akad. Nauk SSSR, Otdel. Khim. Nauk*, **1947**, 435; **1950**, 233; *Izvestia Sektora Fiz.-Khim. Anal., Inst. Obshcheii Neorg. Khim. Akad. Nauk SSSR*, **19**, 256 (1959).

[9] G. C. Schmidt, *Z. physik. Chem.*, **121**, 221 (1926).

pressure of only 3.7 per cent at $x = 0.5$, whereas $CS_2 + C_6H_6$, $\delta_1 - \delta_2 = 0.85$, shows a much larger deviation, 12.2 per cent. The only obvious explanation is that $C_6H_5CH_3$, the stronger base, evokes a little of the acidic character of CS_2 shown in its union with aliphatic sulfides.

LIQUID-LIQUID SOLUBILITY

As remarked earlier, systems with two liquid phases offer the advantage of presenting large derivations from ideality. However, before the advent of fluorocarbons, non-polar components sufficiently unlike to yield two liquid phases were scarce. Hildebrand and Buehrer,[10] in 1920, obtained the consolute temperatures for active phosphorus shown in Table 10.3.

Table 10.3. CRITICAL SOLUTION TEMPERATURES
OF LIQUID PHOSPHORUS, P_4

	t_c °C
n-Decane	390
Chlorobenzene	264
Naphthalene	202
Phenanthrene	200
Anthracene	198
1,2-Dibromethane	165
Carbon disulfide	−6

Another group of liquid-liquid systems was provided with SnI_4 as one component (Table 10.4). Solubility curves with four paraffins, shown in

Table 10.4. CRITICAL SOLUTION TEMPERATURES AND
COMPOSITIONS OF SOLUTIONS OF SnI_4

Second component	t_c °C	$100x_1$ (SnI_4)
n-$C_{32}H_{66}$	194	90
i-C_8H_{18}	195.3	50
n-C_6H_{14}	149.4	42
$SiCl_4$	139.8	41
n-C_7H_{16}	136.8	48
n-C_8H_{18}	132.0	52

[10] J. H. Hildebrand and T. F. Buehrer, *J. Am. Chem. Soc.*, **42**, 2213 (1920).

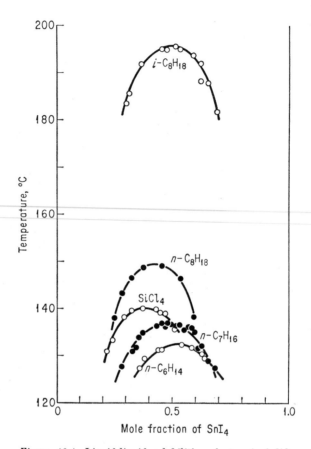

Figure 10.1 Liquid-liquid solubilities of stannic iodide.

Fig. 10.1, were obtained by Miriam Dice.[11] The data for SnI_4 in $SiCl_4$ were obtained by Negishi.[12] The data in Fig. 10.2 for dicetyl, n-$C_{32}H_{66}$, a very long linear molecule, were obtained by Wachter.[13] This is especially interesting because of its extreme asymmetry, to be discussed later.

Hildebrand,[14] in 1937, extrapolated from the solubility of solid I_2 in CCl_4 to predict with good approximation the liquid-liquid system shown in Fig. 10.3 and included in Fig. 9.1. Because the mixtures were quite opaque, the

[11] M. E. Dice and J. H. Hildebrand, *J. Am. Chem. Soc.*, **50**, 3023 (1928).

[12] J. H. Hildebrand and G. R. Negishi, ibid., **59**, 339 (1937).

[13] J. H. Hildebrand and A. Wachter, ibid., **57**, 866 (1935).

[14] J. H. Hildebrand, *J. Am. Chem. Soc.*, **59**, 2083 (1937).

temperatures of separation into two phases were determined by mounting tubes containing mixtures of known composition in a delicately balanced, inclined cradle provided with a mirror which reflected a beam of light upon a scale. The tube and cradle were mounted in an air thermostat. After heating sufficiently to give one liquid phase, the temperature was slowly decreased. At the temperature at which an iodine-rich phase began to form in the lower end of the tube, a torque was registered by the movement of the spot of light on the scale, as illustrated in the insert in Fig. 10.3.

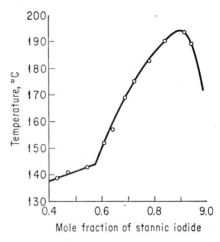

The advent of fluorocarbons provided a new set of non-polar liquids which are only partly mis-cible with other common, non-polar liquids. Hildebrand and Cochran,[15]

Figure 10.2 Liquid-liquid solubility of SnI_4 *with dicetyl, n-$C_{32}H_{66}$.*

in 1949, published solubility curves for c-$C_6F_{11}CF_3$ with CCl_4, $CHCl_3$, C_6H_6, $C_6H_5CH_3$ and C_6H_5Cl. Their results are plotted in Fig. 10.4 vs. mole

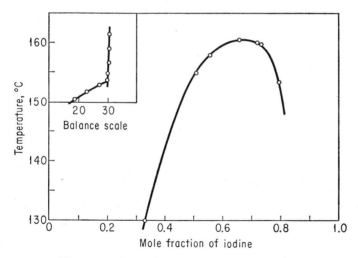

Figure 10.3 Liquid-liquid solubility of I_2 *with* CCl_4.

[15] J. H. Hildebrand and D. R. F. Cochran, *ibid.*, **71**, 22 (1949).

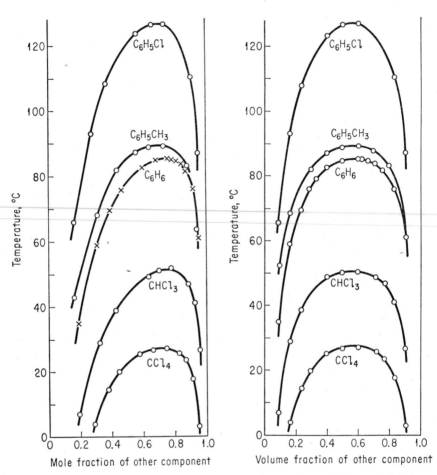

Figure 10.4 Solubility of liquids in
c-$C_6H_{11}CF_3$.

*Figure 10.5 Data in Fig. 9.4 plotted vs.
volume fraction.*

fraction, and in Fig. 10.5 vs. volume fraction. The first of these systems has
since been used in several investigations of its other properties. In 1950,
Hildebrand, Fisher, and Benesi[16] published curves for C_7F_{16} with C_6H_6,
CCl_4, $CHCl_3$, n-C_7H_{16}, and i-C_8H_{18}; they are reproduced here in Figs. 10.6
and 10.7. Closely agreeing values for the mixture with CCl_4 have been
obtained by Kyle and Reed.[17]

[16] J. H. Hildebrand, B. B. Fisher, and H. A. Benesi, *J. Am. Chem. Soc.*, **72**, 7348
(1949).
[17] B. B. Kyle and T. M. Reed, III, *J. Am. Chem. Soc.*, **80**, 6170 (1958).

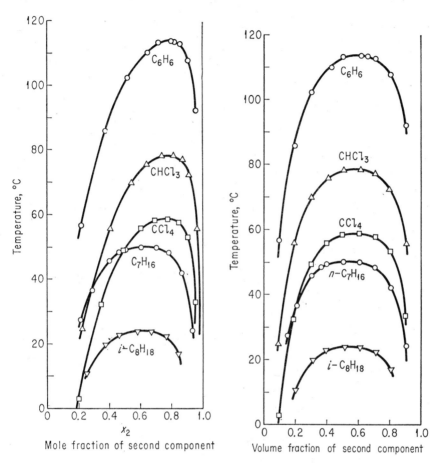

Figure 10.6 Consolute temperatures of perfluoro-n-heptane solutions vs. mole fraction of second component.

Figure 10.7 Consolute temperatures of perfluoro-n-heptane solutions vs. volume fraction of second component.

Solubility curves obtained by other investigators will be referred to in pages to follow. These have been exceedingly useful for the development of regular solution theory. The "regular" additivity of such mixtures is illustrated by the differences of the critical solution temperatures among six mixtures seen in Table 10.5.

There is one respect in which the value of such studies could be considerably enhanced. In nearly all cases, the temperature-composition curves have been carefully determined only in the region of critical temperatures. Systematic comparisons of the results are unsatisfactory for two reasons:

Table 10.5. CORRELATION OF DIFFERENCES
IN CRITICAL TEMPERATURES °C

	CCl$_4$	Diff.	CHCl$_3$	Diff.	C$_6$H$_6$
C$_7$F$_{16}$	58.7	19.8	78.5	35.0	113.5
C$_6$F$_{11}$CF$_3$	26.8	23.5	50.3	35.0	85.3
Diff. 31.9			28.2		28.2

(1) it is difficult to reduce them to a single, standard temperature, and (2) the critical region is just the one where liquid structure is almost intractably complex, and where the simplifying postulate of maximum randomness is inapplicable.

It would be helpful if investigators would determine the composition of the two liquid phases in equilibrium at 25 deg. The large differences between the densities and refractive indices of the pure components offer the means of easy, accurate measurement of equilibrium compositions. Correlations could then be made by taking advantage of the fact that the activity of each component is the same in both liquid phases. Designating these by A and B, respectively, we may write

$$\ln a_{1A} = \ln a_{1B} \quad \text{and} \quad \ln a_{2A} = \ln a_{2B}$$

obtaining

$$\frac{RT}{V_1} \ln \frac{x_{1A}}{x_{1B}} + (\phi_{2A}^2 - \phi_{2B}^2)(\delta_2 - \delta_1)^2 = 0$$

and

$$\frac{RT}{V_2} \ln \frac{x_{2A}}{x_{2B}} + (\phi_{1A}^2 - \phi_{1B}^2)(\delta_2 - \delta_1)^2 = 0$$

Since $\phi_{1A} + \phi_{2A} = 1$ and $\phi_{1B} + \phi_{2B} = 1$, we may add the above equations and simplify to

$$\frac{RT}{2} \left(\frac{1}{V_1} \ln \frac{x_{1B}}{x_{1A}} + \frac{1}{V_2} \ln \frac{x_{2A}}{x_{2B}} \right) = (\phi_{1B} - \phi_{1A})(\delta_2 - \delta_1)^2 \qquad (10.1)$$

An equation of similar form, but expressed throughout in volume fractions, was derived, at the suggestion of Hildebrand, by Rotariu.[18] The change to mole fractions in the left-hand member of Eqn. 10.1 conforms better to present knowledge.

Because liquid-liquid solubility curves involving fluorocarbons are, in general, very unsymmetrical, one branch of the curve has, in most cases, been determined more accurately than the other, and has been carried to a lower temperature. In such cases, where data are insufficient for using

[18] G. J. Rotariu, R. J. Hanrahan, and R. E. Fruin, *J. Am. Chem. Soc.*, **76**, 3752 (1954).

Eqn. 10.1, it is possible to evaluate $\delta_2 - \delta_1$ without serious error from the value of x for the dilute component in that branch, call it x_2, by setting $a_2 \approx 1$, since, in the other branch, $x_2 \approx 1$.

CRITICAL CONSTANTS AND LIQUID-LIQUID MISCIBILITY

Equations for the free energy of mixing, such as Eqn. 7.26 or the analogous equation with the "Flory-Huggins" entropy substituted for the ideal entropy of mixing, can be differentiated to obtain the critical constants T_c and x_c [when $(\partial^2 \Delta F^M / \partial x^2)_{T,P} = (\partial^3 \Delta F^M / \partial x^3)_{T,P} = 0$]. While phenomena in the critical region are much too complex to be accounted for by the simple equations we use, clustering falls off so rapidly as we move away in temperature and composition from T_c and x_c that calculated values of the critical constants cannot be in serious error (more than a few degrees in T or a few hundredths in x). The resulting equations are:

Regular solution:

$$\left(\frac{x_2}{x_1}\right)_c = \frac{(v_1^2 + v_2^2 - v_1 v_2)^{1/2} - v_2}{v_1 - (v_1^2 + v_2^2 - v_1 v_2)^{1/2}} \tag{10.2}$$

$$RT_c = 2A_{12}\left[\frac{(v_1 + v_2)(2v_1^2 - 5v_1 v_2 + 2v_2^2) + 2(v_1^2 - v_1 v_2 + v_2^2)^{3/2}}{27(v_1 - v_2)^2}\right] \tag{10.3}$$

or,

$$RT_c = 2A_{12}\left[\frac{x_1 x_2 v_1^2 v_2^2}{(xv_1 + x_2 v_2)^3}\right] \tag{10.4}$$

Flory-Huggins:

$$\left(\frac{x_2}{x_1}\right)_c = \left(\frac{v_1}{v_2}\right)^{3/2} \tag{10.5}$$

$$RT_c = 2A_{12}\left[\frac{v_1 v_2}{(v_1^{1/2} + v_2^{1/2})^2}\right] \tag{10.6}$$

where, for solubility parameter theory, $A_{12} = (\delta_1 - \delta_2)^2$.

When $v_2/v_1 = 2$, these two sets of equations do not differ greatly (0.007 in x_c, 11 per cent in T_c), so it is only for really large differences in molal volume that it is easy to distinguish between the two.

FLUOROCARBON SOLUTIONS

Scott[19] has used Eqn. 10.2 to infer from critical data the magnitude of the excess free energy and of the interaction constant A_{12} for 34 liquid mixtures of fluorocarbons with

[19] R. L. Scott, *J. Phys. Chem.*, **62**, 136 (1958).

other substances. Table 10.6 compares, for a few of these, the A_{12} determined from critical temperature and from vapor pressures with that calculated from solubility parameters.

Table 10.6. LIQUID-LIQUID SYSTEMS INVOLVING FLUOROCARBONS

System	T-range deg K	T_c deg K	A_{12} (Eqn. 10.1) cal/cc	A_{12} (vapor pressure) cal/cc	$(\delta_1 - \delta_2)^2$ cal/cc
$CF_4 + CH_4$	84–110	95	8.6	8.4	0.6
$CF_4 + Kr$	116	. . .	. . .	7.3	0.0
$C_2F_6 + C_2H_6$	176	. . .	. . .	9.6	0.8
$CF_4 + C_2H_6$	107–151	150	10.9	12.3	0.8
n-$C_6F_{14} + n$-C_6H_{14}	250–314	296	7.0	8.2	2.0
c-$C_6F_{12} + c$-C_6H_{12}	318–343	316	9.1	9.7	4.8
$C_7F_{16} + 2,2,4$-$(CH_3)_3C_5H_9$	284–343	297	6.0	6.7	0.7
$C_7F_{16} + CCl_4$	276–332	332	7.9	. . .	6.8
$CF_3C_6F_{11} + CCl_4$	265–300	300	7.9	. . .	6.8
$CF_3C_6F_{11} + C_6H_6$	308–359	359	9.7	. . .	10.0

Two features are worth noting: (1) where both phase diagrams and free energy data exist, the agreement between the two is only moderately good, and the A_{12} inferred from vapor pressure is almost always the larger. (2) Mixtures of fluorocarbons with certain substances (CCl_4, C_6H_6, etc.) show reasonable agreement with the predictions from their solubilities parameters, as do the solid solubilities of I_2 and SnI_4 (Chapter 9), but with other substances (principally aliphatic hydrocarbons, but also including Kr), the disagreement is extreme.

CONSISTENCY AMONG N-MOLECULES

The theory applies rather well between components of similar electron type and for deviations which are large compared with the inevitable uncertainties. The three liquids, C_7F_{16}, CCl_4, and Br_2, are all N-donors, and their δ-values are widely spread: 5.85, 8.6, and 11.5, respectively.

The vapor pressure of Br_2 from its solution in CCl_4, determined by Lewis and Storch,[20] gives $p_2/p_2^0 = 0.0484$ at $x_2 = 0.025$, at 25 deg whence $\gamma_2 = 1.932$. These figures give, by equation, $\delta_2 - \delta_1 = 2.82$. This is to be compared with $11.5 - 8.6 = 2.9$, a quite satisfactory agreement. The solubility of Br_2 in C_7F_{16} was determined by Reeves and Hildebrand[21] over

[20] G. N. Lewis and H. Storch, *J. Am. Chem. Soc.*, **39**, 2544 (1917).
[21] L. W. Reeves and J. H. Hildebrand, *J. Phys. Chem.*, **60**, 949 (1956).

the range from -5 deg to 25 deg. At 25 deg it is $x_2 = 0.0490$. The reverse solubility is extremely small, so we may set $a_2 \cong 1$, $v_2 = 51.5$, and $v_1 = 225.5$. From these data we calculate $\delta_2 - \delta_1 = 5.94$. This may be compared with their solubility parameters, $11.5 - 5.85 = 5.65$.

For the pair $CCl_4 + C_7F_{16}$, we have the liquid-liquid solubility curve determined by Hildebrand, Fisher, and Benesi,[16] as well as the concordant data of Kyle and Reed.[17] The latter extend to the region of 25 deg. From these we interpolate, in phase A, $x_1 = 0.302$, $\phi_1 = 0.157$; in phase B, $x_1 = 0.969$, $\Phi_1 = 0.930$. And, of course, $x_1 + x_2 = 1$, etc. These figures, substituted in Eqn. 9.1, give $\delta_1 - \delta_2 = 3.05$, in fair agreement with $8.6 - 5.85 = 2.75$. The $\delta_2 - \delta_1$ values for the foregoing three pairs are summarized in Table 10.7. The calculated differences in δ-values agree well with each other and with the values from energy of vaporization.

Table 10.7. ADDITIVITY OF SOLUBILITY PARAMETERS

	$(\delta_2 - \delta_1)$ observed	difference $(\Delta E^V / v)^{1/2}$
$CCl_4 + C_7F_{16}$	3.05	2.75
$Br_2 + CCl_4$	2.82	2.90
Sum	5.87	5.65[a]
$Br_2 + C_7F_{16}$	5.94	5.65[a]

[a] These values necessarily agree.

ANOMALOUS BEHAVIOR OF PARAFFINS

The situation is different in solutions with a paraffin as one component. Figure 10.8 shows the degree of agreement between the $(\Delta E^V / v)^{1/2}$ and δ calculated for $i\text{-}C_8H_{18}$, $n\text{-}C_7H_{16}$, $SiCl_4$, $c\text{-}C_6H_{12}$, CCl_4, $CHCl_3$ and CS_2 from their solubility relations with C_7F_{16}, Br_2, SnI_4, S_8, I_2, and P_4. It will be seen that the δ-value for each of the solvents $SiCl_4$, CCl_4, $CHCl_3$, and CS_2, varies less than 0.3 unit in its several solutions. The solutions of $i\text{-}C_8H_{18} + n\text{-}C_7H_{16}$, on the other hand, give δ-values much larger than $(\Delta E^V / v)^{1/2}$, by about 1.0 for the former and 0.6 for the latter. Each is a better solvent for I_2, etc., and a poorer solvent for fluorocarbons than would be predicted from its "energy density." The fact that the discrepancy is greater for $i\text{-}C_8H_{18}$ than for $n\text{-}C_7H_{16}$ may be significant, especially because it appears to be virtually non-existent in the case of $c\text{-}C_6H_{12}$.

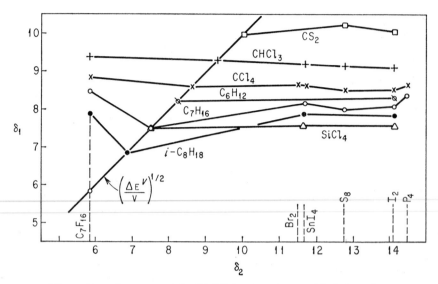

Figure 10.8 Agreement of $(\Delta \text{E}^{\text{V}}/\text{v})^{1/2}$ for six solvents with their δ-values calculated from solubility.

Hildebrand[22] pointed out this irregularity in the solvent characteristics of paraffins in 1950. Rotariu, Hanrahan, and Fruin[18] published liquid-liquid solubility curves for $(C_4F_9)_3N$ with $C_6H_{11}CH_3$, n-C_6H_{14}, and i-C_8H_{18}, respectively; they calculated therefrom $\delta_2 - \delta_1$ values much larger than the differences in their listed solubility parameters. The δ-values of $(C_4F_9)_3N$ and C_7F_{16} are almost identical, 5.90 and 5.85, and the point for $(C_4F_9)_3N$ with i-C_8H_{18} would lie very close to the point for $C_7F_{16} + i$-C_8H_{18} in Fig. 10.8. We have recalculated $\delta_2 - \delta_1$ from their figures for the mixture with i-C_8H_{18} by aid of Eqn. 10.1, and have obtained 2.55. With $(\Delta \text{E}_2^{\text{V}}/v_2)^{1/2}$ = 5.91 = δ_2, for $(C_4H_9)_3N$, we get δ_1 = 8.5 for i-C_8H_{18}, close to the value calculated from its mixture with C_7F_{16}, 8.3, but here again far larger than its value from $(\Delta \text{E}^{\text{V}}/v)^{1/2}$ = 6.85.

Similar discrepancies were found at nearly the same time by Hickman[23] for mixtures of C_7F_{16} with 4 isomeric hexanes; the n-C_6H_{14} is a poorer solvent for C_7F_{16} and a better solvent for I_2. Increasing its solubility parameter by 1.4 would very nearly accord with its solvent power for both I_2 and in C_7F_{16}.

The case of c-$Si_4O_4(CH_3)_8$, superficially a paraffin, is similar. From the solubility of iodine in it (see Chapter 9) $\delta_2 - \delta_1$ = 5.88, and with δ_2 = 14.1,

[22] J. H. Hildebrand, *J. Chem. Phys.*, **18**, 1337 (1950).
[23] J. B. Hickman, *J. Am. Chem. Soc.*, **77**, 6154 (1955).

as usual, we get $\delta_1 = 8.22$, far above the value of $(\Delta E^V / v)^{1/2} = 6.4$. If the latter value were applicable, this substance should form nearly ideal solutions with fluorocarbons instead of two liquid phases, as it does. Jolley and Hildebrand[24] obtained liquid-liquid curves of this siloxane with $C_6F_{11}CF_3$ and with C_7F_{16}. The critical temperatures are 43.86 deg and 69.97 deg, respectively. From the data for the former mixture, which extend to lower temperatures, one can interpolate values of x and ϕ at 35 deg in both phases. Applying Eqn. 10.1 gives $\delta_2 - \delta_1 = 2.06$. Since such differences change but slowly with temperature, we may add $\delta_2 = 6.0$ (25 deg) and get $\delta_1 = 8.06$, nearly the same as the above value for the iodine solution. In other words, a practical value for the solubility parameter of this silicone is ~ 8.1, putting it in company with iso-octane, which is not surprising, since the surfaces of both molecules consist of methyl groups.

Of course, an empirical upward adjustment of the δ-values of aliphatic hydrocarbons does not go to the heart of the problem of the interaction of fluorocarbon molecules with those of other species. Scott[19] has pointed out that this procedure will not account for $CF_4 + CH_4$ (where the δ of methane lies below that of perfluoromethane), and $CF_4 + Kr$, or $C_2F_6 + Xe$, both of which have large A_{12}'s (Table 10.6) in disagreement with $(\delta_1 - \delta_2)^2$. Other proposed explanations of these anomalies, all presumably due to the failure of the geometric mean assumption $c_{12} = (c_{11}c_{22})^{1/2}$, were discussed in Chapter 7.

UNSYMMETRICAL LIQUID-LIQUID SYSTEMS

Nearly all known phase diagrams for systems composed of non-polar liquid components are unsymmetrical when plotted as temperature vs. mole fraction. They are more nearly symmetrical in terms of volume-fraction. This is illustrated in Figs. 10.4 and 10.5. The volume fractions at the critical points, determined on the assumption of rectilinear diameters, are, respectively, 0.60, 0.58, 0.58, 0.53, and 0.54. The same relationships with c-$C_6F_{11}CF_3$ as the common component, shown in Figs. 10.6 and 10.7, are similar.

The asymmetry increases with difference in molal volumes of the components, becoming extreme in the mixtures of $CHCl_3$ and of CCl_4 with $(C_3F_7COOCH_2)_4C$, determined by Shinoda and Hildebrand,[25] shown in Fig. 10.9. The molal volumes at 25 deg of the four liquids involved are

$$CHCl_3, \text{ 81 cc;} \quad CCl_4, \text{ 97 cc;} \quad c\text{-}Si_4O_4(CH_3)_8, \text{ 312 cc;}$$
$$(C_3F_7COOCH_2)_4C, \text{ 542 cc.}$$

The asymmetry is so extreme in the cases of $CHCl_3$, CH_2Cl_2 and CCl_4

[24] J. E. Jolley and J. H. Hildebrand, *J. Phys. Chem.*, **61**, 791 (1957).
[25] K. Shinoda and J. H. Hildebrand, *J. Phys. Chem.*, **62**, 481 (1958).

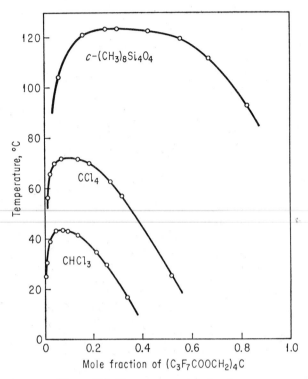

Figure 10.9 Very unsymmetrical systems.

as to afford an additional case for deciding between ideal entropy and "F-H" entropy of mixing,

$$-R \ln x_2 \quad \text{vs.} \quad -R \left(\ln \phi_2 - \phi_1 \frac{1 - v_2}{v_1} \right)$$

The critical composition arising when ideal entropy is combined with a volume fraction dependent energy of mixing is given by Eqn. 10.3. When the "F-H" entropy is used, Eqn. 10.5 is obtained. Table 10.8 gives the

Table 10.8. CRITICAL COMPOSITIONS OF VERY UNSYMMETRICAL SYSTEMS, OBSERVED AND CALCULATED

Components		Mol. vols. at t_c		$(100 x_2)_c$		
1	2	v_1	v_2	Obs.	Eqn. 10.3	Eqn. 10.5
$CHCl_3 + (C_3F_7COOCH_2)_4C$		82.6	553	7.3	7.7	5.5
$CCl_4 + (C_3F_7COOCH_2)_4C$		103.0	571	9.1	9.4	7.1
$CH_2Cl_2 + (C_3F_7COOCH_2)_4C$		65.7	550	5.7	6.1	4.0
$SnI_4 + n\text{-}C_{32}H_{66}$		171.0	615	10.0	15.0	13.0

critical compositions in mole per cent of the ester (1) observed, (2) calculated by Eqn. 10.2, (3) calculated by Eqn. 10.5. It includes, also, the corresponding data by Wachter[4] for SnI_4 in n-$C_{32}H_{66}$, referred to earlier.

We see that the first two mixtures, where both molecular species are fairly compact, conform far better with ideal entropy than with "F-H" entropy, but the fourth mixture, where one component is composed of long, flexible paraffin molecules, agrees much better with "F-H" entropy.

The systems shown in Figs. 10.4 through 10.7 are not sufficiently unsymmetrical to make the difference between the critical compositions calculated by Eqns. 10.2 and 10.5 any larger than the uncertainty in locating the maxima of the curves themselves.

The reciprocal solubilities of $Br_2 + C_7F_{16}$ are extremely unsymmetrical. Reeves and Hildebrand[21] found $x_1 = 5 \times 10^{-2}$ for Br_2 in C_7F_{16}, but for C_7F_{16} in Br_2, x_2 is very roughly 5×10^{-5}. From the simple regular solution equation, one would expect

$$\frac{\log x_1}{\log x_2} = \frac{v_1}{v_2} = \frac{225.5}{51.5} = 4.4$$

and $x_2 = 2 \times 10^{-6}$, an even smaller value than the rough value found.

UNSYMMETRICAL PARTIAL VAPOR PRESSURES

Disparity in molal volumes is associated with asymmetry of all the excess functions. The fact that the potential energy of the mixture (Chapter 7), which governs the asymmetry, is a function of volume fractions rather than mole fractions is clearly demonstrated not only by the form of liquid-liquid solubility curves but also by the forms of total and partial vapor pressure curves.

The molal volumes of CS_2 and i-C_5H_{12} are very different, 60.7 and 117.5, respectively, at 25 deg, and hence ϕ-values differ considerably from x-values. Figure 10.10, line A, illustrates the application of Eqn. 7.28 to the data for partial pressures of mixtures of these two liquids reported by Hirshberg.[26] The solid points refer to CS_2 and the circles to the second component. We see that all points fall close to one straight line: evidence of the applicability of Eqn. 7.27, and also of accurate data consistent with the Gibbs-Duhem equation. Furthermore, the intercept is $5.65 = (\delta_2 - \delta_1)^2$, and $\delta_1 - \delta_2 = 2.82$. With $\delta_1 = 10.0$, $\delta_2 = 7.18$, only a little larger than $(\Delta E^V/v)^{1/2} = 6.75$. The minor discrepancy is in the direction pointed out earlier when one component is a paraffin.

Line B in Fig. 10.10 shows the same treatment of the mixture, $CS_2 + CH_2(OCH_3)_2$, methylal, using data from the classic paper of

[26] J. Hirshberg, *Bull. Soc. Chim. Belg.*, **41**, 163 (1932).

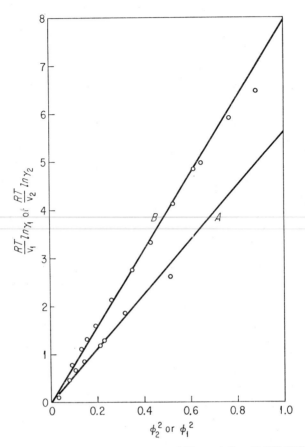

Figure 10.10 Solutions of CS_2 *with, A, i-*C_5H_{12}*, and, B, with* $CH_2(OCH_3)_2$.

Zawidski.[27] Here, too, the data pass the test of consistence. The small scattering of points along the upper end of the line is not significant, as they represent small partial pressures with large percentage errors. The intercept, 8.0, gives $\delta_2 - \delta_1 = 2.82$, larger than $10.0 - 8.2 = 1.8$, which may be explained by the polarity of methylal.

In Fig. 10.11 the data for the same system are plotted, for comparison, as $\log \gamma_1$ vs. x_2^2 and $\log \gamma_2$ vs. x_1^2. They do not fall upon a common straight line, as they should if the system were "strictly regular."

All the data discussed in these last pages are, of course, further evidence in favor of the volume fraction formulation of the potential energy of mixing (Chapter 7).

[27] J. von Zawidski, *Z. physik. Chem.*, **35**, 129 (1900).

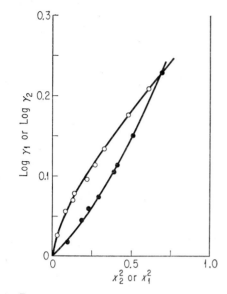

Figure 10.11 The data of line A, Fig. 9.11,   *Figure 10.12 $CS_2 + CHCl_3$ solutions.*
plotted vs. x_1^2, and x_2^2.

The data for the system, $CS_2 + CHCl_3$, also by Hirshberg, plotted in Fig. 10.12, are evidently less accurate than those for $CS_2 + i\text{-}C_5H_{12}$, by the same investigator.

SOLUBILITY OF MERCURY IN LIQUID P_4

Rotariu, Schramke, Gilman, and Hildebrand[28] made a study of solutions of mercury in liquid phosphorus, which included a determination solubility at 25 deg. They found $x_2 = 1.76 \times 10^{-4}$. The solubility parameters are $\delta_1 = 14.5$ and $\delta_2 = 30.7$, and the molal volumes are, respectively, 70.4 cc and 14.8 cc. The solubility is so small that $\ln a_2 \approx 0$, and $\phi_1 \approx 1$. Equation 9.1 gives $x_2 = 1.4 \times 10^{-3}$. This is eight times the observed solubility. It is remarkable that the solubility of a metal in a non-metal in the absence of chemical effects can come even as near as this to the theoretical solubility for a non-metal.

[28] G. J. Rotariu, Eva Schramke, T. S. Gilman, and J. H. Hildebrand, *J. Am. Chem. Soc.*, **73**, 2527 (1951).

CHAPTER 11

Summary and Critique

It seems appropriate to conclude this book by an appraisal of the present status of regular solution theory, with a summary of the items that appear to be based upon substantial evidence and also of questions still awaiting satisfactory answers.

The entropy of mixing non-polar, compact molecules of different species is simpler and more "regular" than the heat of mixing. There is now strong evidence to support the following conclusions:

1. A pure liquid, if composed of non-polar, symmetrical, compact molecules, has a structure of maximum randomness, as represented by the radial distribution function. There is no quasi-crystalline or lattice structure; there are no "holes" of definite size or shape, no discrete molecular frequencies or velocities, and no distinguishable "gas-like" and "solid-like" molecules.

2. The molecules of homogeneous solutions of two non-polar, non-reacting, molecular species may be regarded, for practical purposes, as mixed with maximum randomness except in the immediate neighborhood of their liquid-liquid critical point.

152

3. The partial molal entropy of adding a mole of, say, component 2 to a solution is approximately $-R \ln x_2$ if the solution is allowed to expand only by the molal volume of that component in its pure liquid state, i.e., v_2^o.

4. When that component is added at constant pressure, the usual process, and when the solution expands by the partial molal volume, $\bar{v}_2$ of that component, the partial molal entropy is approximately

$$-R \ln x_2 + (\bar{v}_2 - v_2^o)\left(\frac{\partial P}{\partial T}\right)_v$$

5. Disparity in molal volume, in the case of compact molecules, has virtually no effect upon the entropy of mixing.

6. Because the Gibbs free energy of mixing at constant pressure is virtually identical to the Helmholtz free energy of mixing at constant volume, the excess entropy of solution at constant pressure, due to expansion, is balanced in a regular solution by a corresponding enthalpy of expansion. Consequently, both these corrections can be neglected with little or no error in calculating *isothermal* excess free energies or *isothermal* values of solubility.

This is not true, however, with solutions in which the randomness of molecular distribution is reduced by complexing, making the partial molal entropy of solution less than $-R \ln x_2$.

7. The entropy of solution of gases and their solubilities and temperature coefficients can be predicted for regular solutions from their force constants ϵ/k, as determined from virial coefficients, and the solubility parameters, δ, of the solvents.

8. The entropy of transfer of gases from 1 atmosphere to solutions at equal mole fractions increases strongly with decreasing gas force constants. This is interpreted as being associated with increased freedom of motion of the solvent molecules surrounding the weakly attractive gas molecule.

9. Hydrogen, helium, and neon, in that order, have enhanced solubilities, attributable, perhaps, to the uncertainty principle. This may also account for the 10 per cent excess of the partial molal volume of hydrogen over that of deuterium in benzene and toluene. These facts invite theoretical analysis.

10. The free energies ($\gamma > 1$) of the components of regular solutions are attributable to the fact that attractions between unlike molecules are of smaller magnitude than the average of the attractions between the like molecules. According to the London theory of "dispersion forces" in its original simple form, the attractive potential between unlike molecules is radial and central and involves the geometric mean of the like intermolecular potentials.

11. It is evident, however, that the forces between compact, polyatomic molecules reside mainly in their outer, adjacent portions. Octamethyl-

cyclotetrasiloxane, for example, with its ring of c-Si_4O_4 buried under eight methyl-groups, is much like 2,2,4-tri-methyl pentane ("iso-octane").

12. It is evident, further, that in dealing with intermolecular potentials one should recognize distinct types of molecules:

a. Molecules containing permanent dipoles.

b. Molecules capable of forming hydrogen bonds.

c. Molecules that can act as electron donors or acceptors, i.e., bases and acids in the general scheme of G. N. Lewis.

d. Molecules with π-electrons, including aromatics and olefins.

e. Molecules with outer, non-bonding electron pairs.

f. Molecules with none but bonding electrons, including H_2 and paraffins.

Cases a and b have long been recognized as sources of divergence from regular solution behavior. Specific electron donor-acceptor interaction has also been recognized in cases where it is moderately strong; what has not been fully appreciated is its presence as a disturbing factor in systems usually regarded as normally regular, such as mixtures of carbon tetrachloride with benzene, and of carbon disulfide with benzene and with toluene.

The molecules of the paraffins (case f) which possess only bonding electrons, in many cases behave toward molecules with N-electrons in accordance with solubility parameters considerably greater than the values derived from their attractions for other paraffin molecules.

It seems evident that refinement of the theory of intermolecular potentials must take into account differences in the mutual perturbations between electron orbitals of different types. We suggest the need for investigations of absorption spectra of mixtures of components systematically selected.

13. This book has been devoted essentially to regular solutions, with only casual reference to departures from regularity arising from hydrogen bonds, dipoles, or complexes. The effect of each of these factors is a departure from, and superimposed upon the behavior of, what would otherwise be a regular, not an ideal, solution. All the non-specific interactions are still present.

14. In summation, that part of regular solution theory which deals with entropy seems fairly clear, but the part which deals with energy involves the excess of the potential energies between like molecules over those between unlike molecules, a small difference between large quantities. In the light of variations now apparent in the interaction between molecules of different electron types, it is remarkable that solubility parameters serve as well as they do to predict energies of solution. Further refinements will require something far more basic than mere adjustment of the parameters.

Any satisfying interpretation of liquids and solutions must be a molecular theory and must involve molecular parameters. However, because of the necessary oversimplifications in any theory of the condensed state, how these molecular parameters are evaluated will make a difference. For example, the inexactness of the Lennard-Jones 6-12 potential energy function influences different molecular and thermodynamic properties in different ways. For practical purposes, the most useful theory is likely to be the one which is built "close to the ground," and which evaluates its parameters under conditions closely approximating those where they will be applied. For this reason, we prefer to relate the properties of liquid solutions to those of pure liquids, rather than to dilute gases at very different densities and temperatures.

15. The applicability of regular solution theory to types of systems not treated in this volume was asserted by Professor Leo Brewer in a statement presented in a symposium in Berkeley, September 11-12, 1961, in these words:

It is probably not widely known that the ideas that you [the senior author] developed while working with solutions close to room temperature have been very useful for the understanding of solutions at high temperatures. For example, Flood and his group at Trondheim, Norway have been studying the behavior of fused salts and oxides at high temperatures. They have been able to use your ideas, with slight modifications to take into account the different structure and bonding of ionic melts, to obtain final results which are very close in form to the typical regular solution equations and which have proved remarkably successful in accounting for activity coefficient variations in high temperature solutions. Nowotny and his group in Austria have recently achieved the evaluation of the thermodynamics of the uranium carbides and the elucidation of high temperature solid solution behavior of a number of transition metal carbides through use of the regular solution equations. Many metallic solutions have, surprisingly, shown solution behavior close to the regular solution behavior.

List of Symbols

(*Note:* Minor symbols which occur at only one isolated place in the text are not listed.)

Italic capitals (thermodynamic quantities):

A	Helmholtz free energy
B, C, D	virial coefficients
C	heat capacity
E	energy
F	Gibbs free energy
H	enthalpy, heat content
K	equilibrium constant
N	number of molecules
N_0	Avogadro's number, 6.02×10^{23} molecules/mole
P	pressure
R	gas constant per mole
S	entropy
T	temperature, deg K
V	volume

Small Roman capitals are used for molal and partial molal thermodynamic quantities: e.g., A, C, E, F, H, S, V.

Roman lower case (primarily molecular constants and mathematical symbols):

a	van der Waals attraction constant
b	van der Waals repulsion (volume) constant
c	cohesive energy density ($-$ E/v)
d_0	equilibrium distance of minimum potential energy of a molecular pair
f	function
g	radial distribution function
j	repulsion constant
k	attraction constant
ln	natural logarithm (base e)
log	common logarithm (base 10)
n	ratio of internal pressure to cohesive energy density

Italic lower case:

- a activity
- f fugacity
- k Boltzmann constant, gas constant per molecule
- n number of moles
- p vapor pressure, partial pressure
- r radius, distance variable
- t temperature, deg C
- u potential energy of a pair of molecules
- x mole fraction

Greek capitals:

- Δ increment, a difference function
- Ω number of configurations

Greek lower case:

- α coefficient of thermal expansion
- β coefficient of compressibility
- γ activity coefficient
- δ solubility parameter
- ϵ energy parameter in intermolecular pair potential energy function
- π 3.14159 . . .
- σ collision diameter, distance parameter in intermolecular pair potential energy function
- ϕ volume fraction (see definition in Chapter 2)
- ρ density

Superscripts (processes):

- ^{E} excess
- ^{F} fusion
- ^{M} mixing
- ^{S} sublimation
- ^{T} transition (solid $\alpha \longrightarrow$ solid β)
- ^{V} vaporization

Superscripts (state)

- ^{f} free
- ^{g} gas
- ^{i} ideal
- ^{r} regular
- ^{s} solid
- ^{o} standard (always the pure liquid)

Subscripts:

b	normal boiling point (1 atm pressure)
c	critical point
i, j	general indices
m	mixture; melting point
max	maximum
p, P	constant pressure
r	reduced
t	transition point
u	"unmixed," before mixing, $v_u = x_1 v_1^0 + x_2 v_2^0$
v, V	constant volume
$1, 2, 3$	components

Boldface (electrical)

I	ionization potential
$\boldsymbol{\alpha}$	polarizability
$\boldsymbol{\mu}$	dipole moment

The Acentric Factor and Critical Data

$\omega = -\log P_r - 1.000.$ (P_r is reduced vapor pressure at $T_r = 0.7$)

Substance	$-\log P_r$	ω	T_c (°K)	P_c (atm)
Argon	0.998	−0.002	150.72	48.00
Krypton	0.998	−0.002	209.39	54.182
Simple fluid	(1.000)	(0.000)		
Xenon	1.002	+0.002	289.75	57.636
Methane	1.013	0.013	190.66	45.795
Nitrogen	1.040	0.040	126.26	33.540
Ethane	1.105	0.105	305.75	48.864
Propane	1.152	0.152	369.99	42.011
Neopentane	1.195	0.195	433.76	31.57
n-Butane	1.201	0.201	425.17	37.470
Benzene	1.215	0.215	562.66	48.664
Carbon dioxide	1.225	0.225	304.16	72.800
n-Pentane	1.252	0.252	470.60	33.628
n-Heptane	1.352	0.352	539.94	26.882

K. S. Pitzer, D. Z. Lippmann, R. F. Curl, Jr., C. M. Huggins, and D. E. Peterson, *J. Am. Chem. Soc.*, **77**, 3433 (1955).

Solubility of Gases—$10^4 x_2$, at 25°C and per atm (upper figure) and Entropy of Solution—cal mole^{-1} deg^{-1} (lower figure)

Gas	ε/k	C_7F_{16}	$(C_4F_9)_3N$	$C_6F_{11}CF_3$	$i\text{-}C_8H_{18}$	$n\text{-}C_7H_{16}$	$(C_2H_5)_2O$	$C_6H_{11}CH_3$	$c\text{-}C_6H_{12}$	CCl_4	$C_6H_5CH_3$	C_6H_6	CS_2
He	10	8.90[12] 5.3		7.60[5] ~4.4	3.10[5] 6.3	2.49[5] 6.2		1.57[5]	1.21[5] 8.1			0.78[5,6] 8.9	
Ne	35	14.01[3] 3.7		11.3[5] 2.7	4.6[5] 3.7	3.5[5] 4.4		2.22[5]	1.80[5]			1.1[5,6]	
H_2	37			32.7[7]	7.82[5] 3.3	6.88[3] 3.5	6.27[1] 3.9		3.80[9]	3.19[1,8] 4.5	3.17[3] 4.2	2.58[1,3] 5.1	1.59[1,3] 5.3
N_2	95	38.7[7] -0.6	34.9[12] -0.5				12.47[1] 1.2		7.55[7] 2.1	6.39[1] 2.1		4.42[1,7] 3.3	2.22[7,12] 4.0
CO	100	38.8[9]				17.3[9]	16.8[1]			8.63[1] 1.0	8.1[9]	6.63[1,9] 1.8	3.60[9]
O_2	118	55.3[9]	52.0[12] -1.9		28.1[12] -1.3		19.3[1]			12.0[1] 0.0		8.15[1] 1.2	4.42[9]
Ar	121	54.0[4] -1.6	50.0[12] -1.7	46.0[4] -1.5	29.2[12] -1.8	25.0[5] -1.0		18.55[4] -0.9	14.9[5,6] -0.6	13.44[9] -0.5	10.95[4] 0.4	8.77[5,6] 0.6	4.87[4] 1.8
CH_4	148	82.6[12] -3.4					15.3[1] 2.7		32.7[13]	28.4[1,13] -2.4		20.7[1,13] -1.2	13.12[12] -1.8
Kr	~165	224.3[12] -8.0		83.7[5] -4.9	78.8[5] -4.5	67.6[5] -4.2		57.7[5]	46.7[5] -2.8	64.4[14] -6.8		27.3[5] -1.6	
SF_6	201				153.5[12] -7.4						33.1[14] -5.3		9.24[12] -0.3
CO_2	205	208.8[10] -7.5	200[12] -7.3	160[10]		121[10] -7.9			77[10]	107[10]	105[10]	97[10] -7.4	32.8[10] -4.8
Xe				169[5] ~-7.1	258[5]			230[5]				101[5]	107[9]
C_2H_6	240		333[12] -8.6		294[12] -10.1					208[1,9] -8.8	173[14] -9.7	148[1,9] -7.5	
Cl_2	~300	977[8] -11.5								1650[11] -12.7			

References for Appendix 3

1. J. Horiuti, *Sci. Papers,* Inst. Phys. Chem. Research, Tokyo, **17,** No. 341, 125 (1931).

2. M. W. Cook and D. N. Hanson, Univ. of Calif. Rad. Lab. Report, UCRL 2459 (1954), *Rev. Sci. Inst.,* **28,** 1957.

3. H. W. Cook, D. N. Hansen, and B. J. Alder, *J. Chem. Phys.,* **26,** 748 (1957).

4. L. W. Reeves and J. H. Hildebrand, *J. Am. Chem. Soc.,* **79,** 1313 (1957).

5. H. L. Clever, R. Battino, J. H. Saylor, and P. N. Gross, *J. Phys. Chem.,* **61,** 1078 (1957); **62,** 89, 375 (1958).

6. A. Lannung, *J. Am. Chem. Soc.,* **52,** 68 (1930).

7. J. C. Gjaldbaek and J. H. Hildebrand, *J. Am. Chem. Soc.,* **71,** 3147 (1949).

8. J. C. Gjaldbaek and J. H. Hildebrand, *ibid.,* **72,** 609 (1950).

9. J. C. Gjaldbaek, *Acta Chem. Scand.,* **6,** 623 (1952).

10. J. C. Gjaldbaek, ibid., **8,** 1398 (1954).

11. N. W. Taylor and J. H. Hildebrand, *J. Am. Chem. Soc.,* **45,** 682 (1923).

12. Y. Kobatake and J. H. Hildebrand, *J. Phys. Chem.,* **65,** 331 (1961).

13. A. Lannung and J. C. Gjaldbaek, *Acta Chem. Scand.,* **14,** 1124 (1960).

14. J. H. Hildebrand and G. Archer, *Proc. Nat. Acad. Sci.,* **47,** 1881 (1961).

Solubility of Iodine and Its Dependence
on Temperature at 25°C

Violet Solutions

Solvent	$100x_2$	$R\dfrac{d\log x_2}{d\log T}$ cal/deg	Reference
CS_2	5.58	18.8	A
$CHCl_3$	2.34	20.3	B
$TiCl_4$	2.15	20.7	A
CCl_4	1.417	21.9	C
$c\text{-}C_6H_{12}$	0.918	22.2	D
$c\text{-}(CH_3)_8Si_4O_4$	0.810	22.5	E
$n\text{-}C_7H_{16}$	0.679	23.1	C
$i\text{-}C_8H_{18}$	0.592	23.3	A
$SiCl_4$	0.499	23.3	A
$(CH_3)_3C \cdot C_2H_5$	0.469	23.6	D
$CCl_2F \cdot CClF_2$	0.245	24.4	E
$c\text{-}C_4Cl_2F_6$	0.124	26.2	E
$(C_3F_7COOCH_2)_4C$	0.1170	26.3	E
$(C_4F_9)_3N$	0.0232	~33.0	I
$c\text{-}C_6F_{11}CF_3$	0.0210	33.0	E
$C_8F_{16}O$	0.0208	. . .	I
C_7F_{16}	0.0180	34.0	F

Non-Violet Solutions

C_6H_6	4.80	16.3	C
$p\text{-}C_6H_4(CH_3)_2$	7.66	8.6	D
$1,3,5\text{-}(CH_3)_3C_6H_3$	10.72	11.9	D
$CHBr_3$	6.25	8.2	E
$1,2\text{-}C_2H_4Br_2$	7.82	15.9	D
$1,2\text{-}C_2H_4Cl_2$	2.20	7.1	G
$1,1\text{-}C_2H_4Cl_2$	1.53	8.3	G
$cis\text{-}C_2H_2Cl_2$	1.441	20.9	G
$trans\text{-}C_2H_2Cl_2$	1.417	20.7	G
C_2H_5OH	4.71	7.4	D
$(C_2H_5)_2O$	8.96	7.0	D
$(C_2H_5O)_4Si$	5.75	12.5	E
H_2O	0.241	18.7	H

164

References for Appendix 4

A.   G. R. Negishi, L. H. Donnaly, and J. H. Hildebrand, *J. Am. Chem. Soc.*, **55,** 4793 (1933).

B.   A. Hantzsch and A. Vagt, *Z. physik. Chem.*, **38,** 728 (1901).

C.   J. H. Hildebrand and C. A. Jenks, *J. Am. Chem. Soc.*, **42,** 2180 (1920).

D.   J. H. Hildebrand, H. A. Benesi, and L. M. Mower, *J. Am. Chem. Soc.*, **72,** 1017 (1950).

E.   K. Shinoda and J. H. Hildebrand, *J. Phys. Chem.*, **62,** 292 (1958).

F.   D. N. Glew and J. H. Hildebrand, *J. Phys. Chem.*, **60,** 616 (1956).

G.   H. A. Benesi and J. H. Hildebrand, *J. Am. Chem. Soc.*, **70,** 3978 (1948).

H.   Seidell-Linke, *Solubilities of Inorganic and Metal-Organic Compounds* (D. Van Nostrand and Co., Inc., New York, 1958).

I.   E. P. McLaughlin and R. L. Scott, *J. Am. Chem. Soc.*, **76,** 5276 (1954).

Solubility Parameters

In the latter chapters of this book, we have seen how the thermodynamic properties of solutions depend, to a first approximation, upon the square of the difference between the values of a quantity δ for the two pure liquid components. These δ-values, which we have termed "solubility parameters" because they enable us to predict and interpret solubility in a semi-quantitative manner, are the square roots of the cohesive energy densities:

$$\delta = (-E/v^l)^{1/2} \qquad (A5.1)$$

where $-E$ is the cohesive energy of the liquid, essentially the molal energy of vaporization to the gas at zero pressure (i.e., infinite separation of the molecules), and v^l is the molal volume of the liquid. Since most of the thermodynamic data on solutions use the thermochemical calorie (4.1840 joules) as the energy unit, the solubility parameter normally has the units $(cal\ cm^{-3})^{1/2}$ as in the following table.

There is rarely any difficulty in obtaining a satisfactory value for the molal volume of a liquid, so the evaluation of δ from Eqn. A5.1 is primarily a problem of determining the energy E. Here we briefly summarize some more important methods for obtaining δ-values. Since the theory of the energy of mixing (Chapter 7) is at best approximate, to seek high precision in the evaluation of $(\delta_1 - \delta_2)^2$ is a waste of effort, but it is important to evaluate δ_1 and δ_2 in a consistent way, under similar conditions and at the same temperature.

1. CALCULATION FROM CALORIMETRIC HEATS OF VAPORIZATION

At low vapor pressures, the vapor in equilibrium with the liquid is essentially ideal and we may replace $-E$ by ΔE^V, the energy of vaporization, and

166

that in turn by $\Delta H^V - P \Delta v = \Delta H^V - RT$, where ΔH^V is the heat of vaporization:

$$\delta = \left(\frac{\Delta H^V - RT}{v^l}\right)^{1/2} \tag{A5.2}$$

If the heat of vaporization has been determined calorimetrically at the desired temperature, say 25°C, well below the normal boiling point, it may be substituted directly into Eqn. A5.2 and the solubility parameter may be evaluated. At higher vapor pressures, $P \Delta v$ is not exactly RT and gas law corrections should be applied; in most cases, however, the error, even at the normal boiling point, will be trivial (e.g., even if $P \Delta v = 0.9\, RT$, the error in δ will normally be less than 0.05 units).

(Guggenheim[1] has remarked that the cohesive energy, $-E$, of a liquid consists of two parts, the configurational potential energy E_c of the molecules in their equilibrium positions, and a potential energy vibration which might be approximated by $\frac{3}{2}RT$ per mole. It is the configurational energy which should best fit the geometric mean assumption, so perhaps δ should have been defined in terms of

$$\Delta E^V + \tfrac{3}{2}RT = \Delta H^V + \tfrac{1}{2}RT$$

There is some logic to this criticism, but the actual effect would be to shift all δ-values upward by approximately the same amount, so a change now does not seem worth the effort.)

2. CALCULATION FROM VAPOR PRESSURES

Often no calorimetric measurements have been made, so the heat of vaporization must be calculated from the temperature of the vapor pressure by means of the Clausius-Clapeyron equation:

$$\frac{d \ln p}{dT} = \frac{\Delta H^V}{pT \Delta v^V} = \frac{\Delta H^V_{app}}{RT^2} \tag{A5.3}$$

where Δv^V is the change in volume on vaporization, $v^g - v^l$. We have given the second ΔH^V in Eqn. 3 the subscript *app*, signifying apparent, for this is the true heat of vaporization only at vapor pressures low enough that the vapor is, for all practical purposes, ideal, permitting substitution of RT for $p \Delta v$.

If we define ΔH^V_{app} as $RT^2\, d \ln p/dT$, Eqn. A5.3 can be rearranged as

$$\Delta H^V = \Delta H^V_{app}\left(\frac{p \Delta v^V}{RT}\right) = \Delta H^V_{app} Z \left(\frac{v^g - v^l}{v^g}\right)$$

where Z is the compressibility factor pv^g/RT, which is unity for a perfect gas, but less than unity for real gases below their critical temperatures.

[1] E. A. Guggenheim, private communication.

The energy of vaporization ΔE^V is then

$$\Delta E^V = \Delta H^V - p\,\Delta V^V = (\Delta H_{app}^V - RT)Z\left(\frac{V^g - V^l}{V^g}\right)$$

If we assume the van der Waals expression $E = -a/v$ to make the small correction of ΔE^V to $-E$, we obtain

$$-E = (\Delta H_{app}^V - RT)Z$$

and for the solubility parameter,

$$\delta = \left(\frac{-E}{V^l}\right)^{1/2} = \left[\frac{(\Delta H_{app}^V - RT)Z}{V^l}\right]^{1/2} \qquad (A5.4)$$

For many substances, especially those with large liquid molal volumes V^l, the compressibility factor at the boiling point is distinctly less than unity. This correction for imperfection is not always made, and one should not accept uncritically heats of vaporization based upon vapor pressures, especially in older tables.

3. ESTIMATION FROM THE HILDEBRAND RULE

For many substances, no measured heats of vaporization are available. For non-polar liquids, it is possible to estimate the heat of vaporization from the normal boiling point with the aid of the Hildebrand Rule (cf. Chapter 6). This rule, first proposed in 1915,[2] states that the entropy of vaporization per mole is the same for all normal liquids when compared at temperatures at which their vapors have equal molal volumes. It follows directly from this that the entropy of vaporization (and, consequently, the heat of vaporization likewise) at a temperature T is a universal function of that temperature and the normal boiling point T_b.

The form of this relation cannot be deduced theoretically, but it is easy to obtain empirical relations from the experimental data. From the data on a large number of liquids, mainly hydrocarbons, Scott[3] found, for the heats of vaporization at 25°C and at the normal boiling point, the empirical formulas

$$\Delta H_{298}^V (\text{cal mole}^{-1}) = -2950 + 23.7T_b + 0.020T_b^2 \qquad (A5.5)$$

$$\Delta H_b^V (\text{cal mole}^{-1}) = 17.0T_b + 0.009T_b^2 \qquad (A5.6)$$

This is really a method of interpolating and extrapolating, and where data are available for related compounds, values of ΔH^V estimated from Eqns. A5.5 and A5.6 should be adjusted accordingly.

[2] J. H. Hildebrand, *J. Am. Chem. Soc.*, **37**, 970 (1915); **40**, 45 (1918).

[3] R. L. Scott, unpublished work, reported in J. H. Hildebrand and R. L. Scott, *Solubility of Nonelectrolytes*, 3rd ed. (Reinhold Publishing Corp., 1950), p. 427.

4. ESTIMATION FROM SOLUBILITY DATA

In Chapter 10 we have seen how comparatively consistent values of the solubility parameter may be obtained from measurements of the solubility of a solid in a series of solvents. This is especially useful for solutes with high melting points, since the δ-value for the supercooled liquid can otherwise be obtained only by extensive extrapolation of the properties of the liquid in its normal temperature range.

For empirical purposes, it is frequently convenient to use a solubility parameter for a liquid somewhat different from its "thermodynamic" value $(-\text{E}/\text{v})^{1/2}$. In many cases this is doubtless a crude method of correcting for deviations from the geometric mean law or for imperfectly understood complications of simple solution theory.

Thus, on the average, the solvent power of the polar chloroform fits a δ about 9.0 better than the "thermodynamic" 9.2. Again, Hildebrand has suggested (cf. Chapters 9 and 10), that the aliphatic hydrocarbons frequently behave like solvents with δ-values higher than those calculated from the well-known heats of vaporization. A third example is offered by large globular molecules, where the "practical" solubility parameter is higher than $(-\text{E}/\text{v})^{1/2}$ because the peripheral energy density must exclude the inert "stuffing" contributing to v^l, but not to ΔE^V.

5. OTHER METHODS OF ESTIMATION

Elsewhere[4] we have reviewed other ways of estimating solubility parameters: from the internal pressure $(\partial\text{E}/\partial\text{v})_T$, from equations of state, from critical constants, from optical data. In general, these methods are so much less reliable than those outlined above that they should be avoided if possible.

TEMPERATURE AND PRESSURE DEPENDENCE OF δ

We have seen in Chapters 7 and 8 that the heat of mixing, the excess entropy of mixing, and the volume change on mixing can be deduced from solubility parameter theory with much less success than that found for calculations of the excess free energy. Since the excess entropy $\text{s}^\text{E} = -(\partial F^\text{E}/\partial T)_P$ and the volume change $\text{v}^\text{E} = (\partial F^\text{E}/\partial P)_T$, this poor agreement suggests the futility of trying to calculate δ-values corresponding to the energy and volume at the exact temperature and pressure of the experimental measurement. Not only are temperature and pressure corrections for δ difficult and frequently unre-

[4] J. H. Hildebrand and R. L. Scott, *Solubility of Nonelectrolytes*, 3rd ed. (Reinhold Publishing Corp., 1958), Chap. XXIII, pp. 424–434.

liable; they are virtually worthless even if done carefully. The solubility parameter equations are just "zeroth approximations," and, for the kind of approximate agreement which is all one can expect, it suffices to have self-consistent values of δ for the various components at one temperature, for convenience 25°C, even though the experimental measurement is at quite a different temperature. However, the δ-values should be calculated from data on the liquid below the normal boiling point. The cohesive energy density of a liquid under pressure in a highly expanded state is not a useful parameter in interpreting solutions. "Fictitious" or "empirical" solubility parameters for low boiling liquids could be referred to 25°C for comparison purposes, but these bear no relation to any real properties of the pure "liquid" at this temperature.

SOLUBILITY PARAMETERS OF POLAR SUBSTANCES

Since the justification for the geometric mean law and solubility parameter theory rests upon the London theory of dispersion forces, the use of solubility parameters for polar substances is somewhat questionable. It is evident, however, that when the dipole is reasonably well buried within the molecule and specific directional forces are unimportant, the solubility parameter may still be a useful concept. For example, the cohesive energy densities of diethyl ether, chloroform, methylene iodide, etc., yield solubility parameters which correspond reasonably well with the solvent power towards other liquids which are non-polar. However, the general use of δ-values for esters, ketones, alcohols, etc. should be avoided. "Solubility parameters" of many polar substances have been tabulated by Burrell,[5] who, however, warns his readers about the questionable nature of their use.

[5] H. Burrell, *Interchem. Rev.* **14**, 3, 31 (1955).

Selected Values of Solubility Parameters at 25°C

The heats of vaporization, where possible, are corrected to vaporization to the ideal gas state (the "standard heat of vaporization"). For substances which are solids at 25°C, the values are extrapolated ones for the supercooled liquids. These are the "thermodynamic" solubility parameters and, as indicated in the text (Chapters 9 and 10) are not always appropriate for solutions.

Formula	Substance	V_{298} (cm^3)	ΔH_{298}^V (kcal)	δ (cal$^{1/2}$ cm$^{-3/2}$)
	ELEMENTS			
Br$_2$	bromine	51	7.34	11.5
I$_2$	iodine	59		14.1
S$_8$	sulfur	135		12.7
P$_4$	phosphorus	70	12.6	13.1
	TETRAHALIDES			
CCl$_4$	carbon tetrachloride	97	7.83	8.6
SiCl$_4$	silicon tetrachloride	115	7.19	7.6
SiBr$_4$	silicon tetrabromide	127	10.38	8.8
GeCl$_4$	germanium tetrachloride	115	8.09	8.1
SnCl$_4$	stannic chloride	118	9.55	8.7
SnI$_4$	stannic iodide	151	19.63	11.7
	OTHER INORGANIC COMPOUNDS			
OsO$_4$	osmium tetroxide	58	9.80	12.6
MoF$_6$	molybdenum hexafluoride	84	6.36	8.3
WF$_6$	tungsten hexafluoride	88	6.25	8.0
UF$_6$	uranium hexafluoride	96	7.2	8.9
Si(CH$_3$)$_4$	silicon tetramethyl	136	5.80	6.2
	ALIPHATIC HYDROCARBONS			
C$_5$H$_{12}$	n-pentane	116	6.40	7.1
	2-methyl butane (isopentane)	117	6.03	6.8
	2,2-dimethyl propane (neopentane)	122	5.35	6.2
C$_6$H$_{14}$	n-hexane	132	7.57	7.3
C$_7$H$_{16}$	n-heptane	148	8.75	7.4
C$_8$H$_{18}$	n-octane	164	9.92	7.5
	2,2,4-trimethylpentane ("isooctane")	166	8.40	6.9
C$_{16}$H$_{34}$	n-hexadecane	294	19.38	8.0

Formula	Substance	V_{298} (cm³)	ΔH_{298}^V (kcal)	δ (cal$^{1/2}$ cm$^{-3/2}$)
C_5H_{10}	cyclopentane	95	6.85	8.1
C_6H_{12}	cyclohexane	109	7.91	8.2
C_7H_{14}	methylcyclohexane	128	8.46	7.8
C_6H_{12}	1-hexene	126	7.34	7.3
C_8H_{16}	1-octene	158	9.70	7.6
C_6H_{10}	1,5-hexadiene	118	7.6	7.7
	AROMATIC HYDROCARBONS			
C_6H_6	benzene	89	8.10	9.2
C_7H_8	toluene	107	9.08	8.9
C_8H_{10}	ethylbenzene	123	10.10	8.8
	o-xylene	121	10.38	9.0
	m-xylene	123	10.20	8.8
	p-xylene	124	10.13	8.8
C_9H_{12}	n-propyl benzene	140	11.05	8.6
	mesitylene	140	11.35	8.8
C_8H_8	styrene	116	10.5	9.3
$C_{10}H_8$	naphthalene	123		9.9
$C_{14}H_{10}$	anthracene	(150)		9.9
$C_{14}H_{10}$	phenanthrene	158		9.8
	FLUOROCARBONS			
C_6F_{14}	perfluoro-n-hexane	205	7.75	5.9
C_7F_{16}	perfluoro-n-heptane (pure)	226	8.69	6.0
	perfluoroheptane (mixture)			5.85
C_6F_{12}	perfluorocyclohexane	170	6.9	6.1
C_7F_{14}	perfluoro (methylcyclohexane)	196	7.9	6.1
	OTHER FLUOROCHEMICALS			
$(C_4F_9)_3N$	perfluoro tributylamine	360	13.0	5.9
$C_4Cl_2F_6$	dichlorohexafluoro-cyclobutane	142		7.1
$C_4Cl_3F_7$	2,2,3-trichloroheptafluoro butane	165	8.51	6.9
$C_2Cl_3F_3$	1,1,2-trichloro, 1,2,2-trifluoroethane	120	7.9	7.3
$C_7F_{15}H$	pentadecafluoroheptane	215	9.01	6.3
	OTHER ALIPHATIC HALOGEN COMPOUNDS			
CH_2Cl_2	methylene chloride	64	6.84	9.8
$CHCl_3$	chloroform	81	7.41	9.2
CCl_4	carbon tetrachloride	97	7.83	8.6
$CHBr_3$	bromoform	88	10.3	10.5
CH_3I	methyl iodide	63	6.7	9.9
CH_2I_2	methylene iodide	81		11.8
C_2H_5Cl	ethyl chloride	74	5.7	8.3
C_2H_5Br	ethyl bromide	75	6.5	8.9
C_2H_5I	ethyl iodide	81	7.7	9.4

Formula	Substance	V_{298} (cm³)	ΔH^V_{298} (kcal)	δ (cal$^{1/2}$ cm$^{-3/2}$)
$C_2H_4Cl_2$	1,2 dichloroethane (ethylene chloride)	79	8.3	9.9
$C_2H_4Cl_2$	1,1 dichloroethane (ethylidene chloride)	85	7.7	9.1
$C_2H_4Br_2$	1,2 dibromoethane	90	9.9	10.2
$C_2H_3Cl_3$	1,1,1 trichloroethane	100	7.8	8.5
$C_2H_2Cl_2$	*cis*-1,2 dichloroethylene	76	6.9	9.1
	trans-1,2 dichloroethylene	78	6.8	9.0
C_2Cl_4	tetrachloroethylene	103	9.5	9.3

OTHER ALIPHATIC COMPOUNDS

Formula	Substance	V_{298} (cm³)	ΔH^V_{298} (kcal)	δ (cal$^{1/2}$ cm$^{-3/2}$)
CS_2	carbon disulfide	61	6.7	10.0
$C_3H_8O_2$	dimethoxymethane (methylal)	89	6.6	8.2
$C_4H_{10}O$	diethyl ether	105	6.36	7.4

Author Index

Subject Index